AND TECHNOLOGY

Edited by
Jack Bemporad · Abraham Segal
Jack D. Spiro · Robert S. Widom

Of the earth's many critters
With their various sized litters
All did eat and were stalked or were stalking
But the queerest of all
Was the brain that stood tall
And not only was eating, but talking!

Union of American Hebrew Congregations

With his words, man saw more
Than ever before
For he saw what his eyes couldn't see
For his words were like lenses
That saw more than his senses
So whatever he talked could be!

Man's words were so clever
They served as a lever
To pry the lid off the unknown.
Soon man was so zealous
As to what words could tell us,
He listened without being shown.

One day man invented
A word he pretended
Was mighty, all knowing, and good.
And he claimed that this word
Was one that he heard
When praying as everyone should.

But the word that he heard
As he tended his herd
Was not the same word as his brother
Had heard in his sleep
While counting his sheep
So they merely confused one another.

(cont'd on inside back cover)

INTRODUCTION

The essays in this unit deal with the relationship of science and technology to ethical and religious values. Although they are written from differing perspectives and in no sense express unanimity of opinion, they agree in stressing the enormous importance of science and technology for the future of mankind. Whether one exults in technological innovation or reacts with foreboding, no one minimizes its importance. The goal of these essays is to examine the moral problems that science and technology raise in our time.

Although everyone is certain that science and technology will have a great impact on the future, there is little agreement among scientists and technologists as to what that future will be and how it will affect our inner life. This is the essential concern of these essays, which focus on the following basic questions:

1. What does the scientific view of nature mean for man and his values?

2. How has technology concretized the world view of science, thereby giving it stupendous power over man and his destiny?

3. In a technological world, who is in control—man or machine?

4. How can Judaism, in the face of technological innovation, reaffirm its values and its traditional teachings about man's freedom and power?

5. How can Judaism help us accept the things that are valuable in science and technology in order to use them to serve religious ends?

6. Can science and technology fit into Jewish religious perspective, or are the two disparate and alien to each other?

The essays and additional material in this course discuss these questions in detail. The essays are by no means easy to read. However, only through exploring the crucial questions these essays raise can we hope to find the means of resolving a basic dilemma of our times for good rather than for evil.

The Editors

$E = MC^2$

What was our trust, we trust not,
What was our faith, we doubt;
Whether we must or not
We may debate about.
The soul, perhaps, is a gust of gas
And wrong is a form of right—
But we know that Energy equals Mass
By the Square of the Speed of Light.

What we have known, we know not,
What we have proved, abjure.
Life is a tangled bowknot,
But one thing still is sure.
Come, little lad; come, little lass,
Your docile creed recite:
"We know that Energy equals Mass
By the Square of the Speed of Light."

Morris Bishop

ACKNOWLEDGMENTS

For permission to reprint the copyrighted selections in this volume, thanks are due to the following authors and publishers:

ESSAYS

Barnes & Noble, Inc., New York: "A Free Man's Worship" from *Mysticism and Logic,* by Bertrand Russell.

Bulletin of the Atomic Scientists, Chicago: "Can Technology Replace Social Engineering?" by Alvin Weinberg; "Ethics of the Scientific Age," by W. Heitler; "Ethics for the Scientist," by John Haybittle.

The Center Magazine, Santa Barbara, California: "The Technophiliacs," by W. H. Ferry.

Dimension, New York: "Judaism and Scientific Thought," by Jack Bemporad.

Doubleday & Company, Inc., New York: "What Man Can Make of Man," by Karl H. Hertz from *Changing Man: The Threat and the Promise,* edited by Kyle Haselden and Philip Hefner; "Scientists Are Stupid!" by John W. Campbell from *Analog 5,* edited by John W. Campbell.

Judaism, A Quarterly Journal, New York: "Science and Creation," by William Etkin.

Meredith Press, New York: "Where Religion and Science Meet," by Roland B. Gittelsohn from *Religion Ponders Science,* edited by Edwin Booth.

The *New York Times,* New York: "Can the World Be Saved?" by LaMont C. Cole.

Philosophical Library, New York: "Science and Religion," from *Ideas and Opinions* by Albert Einstein, published by Crown Publishers, Inc.

Random House, Inc., New York: "The Bird and the Machine" from *The Immense Journey,* by Loren Eiseley.

The Reconstructionist, New York: "Science vs. Religion in the 20th Century," by Harry Posner.

Saturday Review, New York: "What Would a Scientific Religion Be Like?" by H. G. MacPherson.

Think Magazine, Armonk, New York: "The Convergence of Science and Religion," by Charles H. Townes, published by IBM, copyright 1966 by Charles H. Townes.

POEMS

Thomas Y. Crowell Company, New York: "Lines Written after the Discovery by the Author of the Germ of Yellow Fever" by Ronald Ross, from *Imagination's Other Place* compiled by Helen Plotz.

Education: "Teaching Machine" by Norman H. Russell, 88.2, p. 111.

Faber and Faber, Ltd., London: "The Dunce" by Walter de la Mare.

Harvard University Press: "Entropy" from *Acre in the Seed* by Theodore Spencer, copyright 1949.

Holt, Rinehart & Winston, Inc., New York: "Richard Tolman's Universe" by Leonard Bacon and "Innate Helium" by Robert Frost.

Journal of Creative Behavior: "Boo and Hoohoo" by Bert Decker, 3.1, Winter 1969.

The Macmillan Company, New York: "What Am I, Life?" by John Masefield from *Imagination's Other Place,* copyright 1916, 1944, John Masefield.

The New Yorker: "It Rolls On," copyright 1930, Morris Bishop, originally in *The New Yorker,* and "E = MC^2" by Morris Bishop, copyright 1946 *The New Yorker Magazine, Inc.*

Random House, Inc. and Alfred A. Knopf, Inc., New York: "A Man Said to the Universe" by Stephen Crane.

The Reader's Digest and Mrs. Gene Arthur: "Graffiti on a Washroom Wall at M.I.T."

Union of Liberal and Progressive Synagogues, London: *"Avodat Halev"* by Norman Corwin from *On a Note of Triumph,* 1967.

Yale University Press, New Haven, Connecticut: "The Laboratory Midnight," from *The Connecticut River and Other Poems,* by Reuel Denney, copyright 1939, Yale University Press.

PHOTOGRAPHS

American Museum of Natural History, p. 19; Hayden Planetarium, pp. ii, iii; Keystone Press Agency, pp. 73, 91, 111, 127, 143; NASA, cover; Pennsylvania State University, pp. 3, 127 (inset); Photo World, p. 33; United Nations, p. 53; Wide World Photo, p. 157(2).

CONTENTS

"A MAN SAID TO THE UNIVERSE"

A man said to the universe:
"Sir, I exist!"
"However," replied the universe,
"The fact has not created in me
A sense of obligation."

Stephen Crane

Part I

SCIENCE AND THEOLOGY

BEFORE YOU READ—

*THE
CONVERGENCE
OF
SCIENCE
AND
RELIGION,
by Townes*

Ask yourself:

1. Are scientists ever religious?

2. Can a religious person be scientific?

3. Does science or religion have more influence on your personal life?

4. Do you feel any personal conflicts between Judaism and science?

5. Can you prove everything you know?

6. Is truth the same thing in science and religion?

7. If you know enough facts, will you have the "absolute truth"?

8. Is Judaism a "true" religion? If it is, are other religions "false"?

9. Do religious people ever have doubts?

10. Is science always right?

11. Can technology be dangerous?

12. Does science require revelation, faith, or belief?

13. Does science have anything to do with ethics and morality?

14. Does our universe have a purpose?

THE CONVERGENCE OF SCIENCE AND RELIGION

Charles H. Townes

The author argues that scientific and religious thought, far from conflicting, are today finding more and more in common and are destined ultimately to merge.

THE EVER-INCREASING SUCCESS of science has posed many challenges and conflicts for religion—conflicts which are resolved in individual lives in a variety of ways. Some accept both religion and science as dealing with quite different matters by different methods, and thus separate them so widely in their thinking that no direct confrontation is possible. Some repair rather completely to the camp of science or of religion and regard the other as ultimately of little importance, if not downright harmful.

To me, science and religion are both universal, and basically very similar. In fact, to make the argument clear, I should like to adopt the rather extreme point of view that their differences are largely superficial, and that the two become almost indistinguishable if we look at the real nature of each. It is perhaps science whose real nature is the less obvious, because of its blinding superficial successes. To explain this, and to give perspective to the nonscientists, we must consider a bit of the history and development of science.

The march of science during the nineteenth century produced enormous confidence in its success and generality. One field after another fell before the objective inquiry, experimental approach, and the logic of science. Scientific laws appeared to take on an absolute quality, and it was very easy to be convinced that science in time would explain everything.

This was the time when Laplace could believe that if he knew the position and velocity of every particle in the universe, and could calculate sufficiently well, he would then know the entire future. Laplace was simply expressing the evident experience of the time, that the success and precision of scientific laws had changed determinism from a speculative argument to one which seemed inescapable.

This was the time when the devout Pasteur, asked how he as a scientist could be religious, simply replied that his laboratory was one realm and that his home and religion were a completely different one.

SCIENTIFIC ABSOLUTISM

There are today many vestiges of this nineteenth-century scientific absolutism in our thinking and attitudes. It has given Communism, based on Marx's nineteenth-century background, some of its sense of the inexorable course of history and of "scientific" planning of society.

Towards the end of the nineteenth century, many physical scientists viewed their work as almost complete and needing only some extension and more detailed refinement. But soon after, deep problems began to appear. The world seems relatively unaware of how deep these problems really were, and of the extent to which some of the most fundamental scientific ideas have been overturned by them. Perhaps this unawareness is because science has been vigorous in

4

changing itself and continuing to press, and has also diverted attention by ever more successes in solving the practical problems of life.

Many of the philosophical and conceptional bases of science have in fact been disturbed and revolutionized. The poignancy of these changes can be grasped only through sampling them. For example, the question whether light consists of small particles shot out by light sources or wave disturbances originated by them had been debated for some time by the great figures of science. The question was finally settled in the early nineteenth century by brilliant experimentation which could be thoroughly interpreted by theory. The experiments told scientists of the time that light was unequivocally a wave and not particles. But about 1900, other experiments turned up which showed just as unequivocally that light is a stream of particles rather than waves. Thus physicists were presented with a deeply disturbing paradox. Its solution took several decades, and was only accomplished in the mid-1920s by the development of a new set of ideas known as quantum mechanics.

The trouble was that scientists were thinking in terms of their common everyday experience and that experience encompassed the behavior of large objects, but not yet many atomic phenomena. Examination of light or atoms in detail brings us into a new realm of very small quantities with which we have had no previous experience, and where our intuitions could well be untrustworthy. And now in retrospect, it is not at all surprising that the study of matter on the atomic scale has taught us new things, and that some are inconsistent with ideas which previously had seemed so clear.

Physicists today believe that light is neither precisely a wave nor a particle, but both; and we were mistaken in even asking the question, "Is light a particle or is it a wave?" It can display both properties. So can all matter, including baseballs and locomotives. We don't ordinarily observe this duality in large objects because they do not show wave properties prominently. But in principle we believe they are there.

We have come to believe other strange phenomena as well. Suppose an electron is put in a long box where it may travel back and forth. Physical theory now tells us that, under certain conditions, the electron will be sometimes found towards one end of the box and sometimes towards the other, but never in the middle. This statement clashes absurdly with ideas of an electron moving back and forth, and yet most physicists today are quite convinced of its validity, and can demonstrate its essential truth in the laboratory.

THE UNCERTAINTY PRINCIPLE

Another strange aspect of the new quantum mechanics is called the uncertainty principle. This principle shows that if we try to say exactly where a particle (or object) is, we cannot say exactly how fast it is going and in what direction, all at the same time; or, if we determine its velocity, we can never say exactly what its position is. And so, according to this theory, Laplace was wrong from the beginning. If he were alive today, he would probably understand along with other contemporary physicists that it is fundamentally impossible to obtain the information necessary for his precise predictions, even if he were dealing with only one single particle, rather than the entire universe.

The modern laws of science seem, then, to have turned our thinking away from complete determinism and towards a world where chance plays a major role. It is chance on an atomic scale, but there are situations and times when the random change in position of one atom or one electron can materially affect the large-scale affairs of life and, in fact, our entire society. A striking example involves Queen Victoria who, through one such event on an atomic scale, became a mutant and passed on to certain male descendants in Europe's royal families the trait of hemophilia. Thus one unpredictable event on an atomic scale had its effect on both the Spanish royal family and, through an afflicted czarevitch, on the stability of the Russian throne.

EINSTEIN AND CHANCE

This new view of a world which is not predictable from physical laws was not at all easy for physicists of the older tradition to accept. Even Einstein, one of the architects of quantum mechanics, never completely accepted the indeterminism of chance which it implies. This is the origin of his intuitive response, "Herr Gott würfelt nicht"—"The Lord God doesn't throw dice." It is interesting to note also that Russian Communism, with its roots in nineteenth-century determinism, for a long time took a strong doctrinaire position against the new physics of quantum mechanics.

When scientists pressed on to examine still other realms outside our common experience, further surprises were found. For objects of much higher velocities than we ordinarily experience, relativity shows that very strange things happen. First, objects can never go faster than a certain speed, regardless of how hard they are pushed. Their absolute maximum speed is that of light—186,000 miles per second. Further, when objects are going fast, they become shorter and more massive—they change shape and also weigh more. Even time moves at a different rate; if we send a clock off at a high velocity, it runs slower.

THE CAT-KITTEN CONCEPT

This peculiar behavior of time is the origin of the famous cat-kitten conceptual experiment. Take a litter of six kittens and divide them into two groups. Keep three of them on earth, send the other three off in a rocket at a speed nearly as fast as light, and after one year bring them back. The earth kittens will obviously have become cats, but the ones sent into space will have remained kittens. This theory has not been tested with kittens, but it has been checked experimentally with the aging of inanimate objects and seems to be quite correct. Today the vast majority of scientists believe it true.

How wrong, oh how wrong were many ideas which physicists felt were so obvious and well-substantiated at the turn of the century!

Scientists have now become a good deal more cautious and modest about extending scientific ideas into realms where they have not yet been thoroughly tested. Of course, an important part of the game of science is in fact the development of general laws that can be extended into new realms. These laws are often remarkably successful in telling us new things or in predicting things which we have not yet directly observed. And yet we must always be aware that such extensions may be wrong, and wrong in very fundamental ways. In spite of all the changes in our views, it is reassuring to note that the laws of nineteenth-century science were not so far wrong in the realm in which they were initially applied—that of ordinary velocities and of objects larger than the point of a pin. In this realm they were essentially right, and we still teach the laws of Newton or of Maxwell, because in their own important sphere they are valid and useful.

We know today that the most sophisticated present scientific theories, including modern quantum mechanics, are still incomplete. We use them because in certain areas they are so amazingly right. Yet they lead us at times into inconsistencies which we do not understand, and where we must recognize that we have missed some crucial ideas. We simply admit and accept the paradoxes and hope that sometime in the future they will be resolved by a more complete understanding. In fact, by recognizing these paradoxes clearly and studying them, we can perhaps best understand the limitations in our thinking and correct them.

With this background on the real state of scientific understanding, we come now to the similarity and near identity of science and religion. The goal of science is to discover the order in the universe, and to understand through it the things we sense around us, and even man himself. This order we express as scientific principles or laws, striving to state them in the simplest and yet most inclusive ways. The goal of religion may be stated, I believe, as an understanding (and hence acceptance) of the purpose and meaning of our universe and how we fit into it. Most religions see a unifying and inclusive origin of meaning, and this supreme purposeful force we call God.

Understanding the *order* in the universe and understanding the *purpose* in the universe are not identical, but they are also not very far apart. It is interesting that the Japanese word for physics is *butsuri*, which translated means simply *the reasons for things*. Thus we readily and inevitably link closely together the nature and the purpose of our universe.

What are the aspects of religion and science which often make them seem

7

almost diametrically opposite? Many of them come, I believe, out of differences in language used for historical reasons, and many from quantitative differences which are large enough that unconsciously we assume they are qualitative ones. Let us consider some of these aspects where science and religion may superficially look very different.

THE ROLE OF FAITH

The essential role of faith in religion is so well-known that taking things on faith rather than proving them is usually taken as characteristic of religion, and as distinguishing religion from science. But faith is essential to science too, although we do not so generally recognize the basic need and nature of faith in science.

Faith is necessary for the scientist even to get started, and deep faith necessary for him to carry out his tougher tasks. Why? Because he must have confidence that there is order in the universe and that the human mind—in fact his own mind—has a good chance of understanding this order. Without this confidence, there would be little point in intense effort to try to understand a presumably disorderly or incomprehensible world. Such a world would take us back to the days of superstition, when man thought capricious forces manipulated his universe. In fact, it is just this faith in an orderly universe, understandable to man, which allowed the basic change from an age of superstition to an age of science, and has made possible our scientific progress.

The necessity of faith in science is reminiscent of the description of religious faith attributed to Constantine: "I believe so that I may know." But such faith is now so deeply rooted in the scientist that most of us never even stop to think that it is there at all.

Einstein affords a rather explicit example of faith in order, and many of his contributions come from intuitive devotion to a particularly appealing type of order. One of his famous remarks is inscribed in German in Fine Hall at Princeton: "God is very subtle, but He is not malicious." That is, the world which God has constructed may be very intricate and difficult for us to understand, but it is not arbitrary and illogical. Einstein spent the last half of his life looking for a unity between gravitational and electromagnetic fields. Many physicists feel that he was on the wrong track, and no one yet knows whether he made any substantial progress. But he had faith in a great vision of unity and order, and he worked intensively at it for thirty years or more. Einstein had to have the kind of dogged conviction that could have allowed him to say with Job, "Though He slay me, yet will I trust in Him."

For lesser scientists, on lesser projects, there are frequent occasions when things just don't make sense, and making order and understanding out of one's work seems almost hopeless. But still the scientist has faith that there is order to be found, and that either he or his colleagues will someday find it.

THE ROLE OF REVELATION

Another common idea about the difference between science and religion is based on their methods of discovery. Religion's discoveries often come by great revelations. Scientific knowledge, in the popular mind, comes by logical deductions, or by the accumulation of data which is analyzed by established methods in order to draw generalizations called laws. But such a description of scientific discovery is a travesty on the real thing. Most of the important scientific discoveries come about very differently and are much more closely akin to revelation. The term itself is generally not used for scientific discovery, since we are in the habit of reserving revelation for the religious realm. In scientific circles one speaks of intuition, accidental discovery, or says simply that "he had a wonderful idea."

If we compare how great scientific ideas arrive, they look remarkably like religious revelation viewed in a nonmystical way.

Think of Moses in the desert, long troubled and wondering about the problem of saving the children of Israel, when suddenly he had a revelation by the burning bush.

Consider some of the revelations of the New Testament.

Think of Gautama Buddha who traveled and inquired for years in an effort to understand what was good, and then one day sat down quietly under a Bo tree where his great ideas were revealed.

Similarly, the scientist, after hard work and much emotional and intellectual commitment to a troubling problem, sometimes suddenly sees the answer. Such ideas much more often come during off-moments than while confronting data.

A striking and well-known example is the discovery of the benzene ring by Kékulé, who while musing at his fireside was led to the idea by a vision of snakes taking their tails in their mouths. We cannot describe the human process which leads to the creation of an important and substantially new scientific insight. But it is clear that the great scientific discoveries, the real leaps, do not usually come from the so-called "scientific method," but rather more as did Kékulé's—with perhaps less picturesque imagery, but by revelations which are just as real.

Another popular view of the difference between science and religion is based on the notion that religious ideas depend only on faith and revelation while science succeeds in actually proving its points. In this view, proofs give to scientific ideas a certain kind of absolutism and universalism which religious ideas have only in the claims of their proponents. But the actual nature of scientific "proof" is rather different from such simple ideas.

PROVING A SET OF POSTULATES

Mathematical or logical proof involves choice of some set of postulates, which hopefully are consistent with one another and which apply to a situation of interest. In the case of natural science, they are presumed to apply to the world around us. Next, on the basis of agreed-on laws of logic, which must be assumed, one can derive or "prove" the consequences of these sets of postulates.

How can we be sure the postulates are satisfactory? The mathematician Gödel has shown that, in the most generally used mathematics, it is fundamentally impossible to know whether or not the set of postulates chosen are even self-consistent. Only by constructing and using a new set of master postulates can we test the consistency of the first set. But these in turn may be logically inconsistent without the possibility of our knowing it. Thus we never have a real base from which we can reason with surety. Gödel doubled our surprises by showing that, in this same mathematical realm, there are always mathematical truths which fundamentally cannot be proved by the approach of normal logic. His important proofs came only about three decades ago, and have profoundly affected our view of human logic.

There is another way by which we become convinced that a scientific idea or postulate is valid. In the natural sciences, we "prove" it by making some kind of test of the postulate against experience. We devise experiments to test our working hypotheses, and believe those laws or hypotheses are correct which seem to agree with our experience. Such tests can disprove an hypothesis, or can give us useful confidence in its applicability and correctness, but never proof in any absolute sense.

Can religious beliefs also be viewed as working hypotheses, tested and validated by experience? To some this may seem a secular and even an abhorrent view. In any case, it discards absolutism in religion. But I see no reason why acceptance of religion on this basis should be objectionable. The validity of religious ideas must be and has been tested and judged through the ages by societies and by individual experience. Is there any great need for them to be more absolute than the law of gravity? The latter is a working hypothesis whose basis and permanency we do not know. But on our belief in it, as well as on many other complex scientific hypotheses, we risk our lives daily.

Science usually deals with problems which are so much simpler and situations which are so much more easily controllable than does religion that the quantitative difference in directness with which we can test hypotheses generally hides the logical similarities which are there. The controlled experiment on religious ideas is perhaps not possible at all, and we rely for evidence primarily on human history and personal experience. But certain aspects of natural science, and the extension of science into social sciences, have also required similar use of experience and observation in testing hypotheses instead of only easily reproducible experiments.

Suppose now that we were to accept completely the proposition that science and religion are essentially similar. Where does this leave us and where does it lead us? Religion can, I believe, profit from the experience of science where the hard facts of nature and the tangibility of evidence have beaten into our thinking some ideas which mankind has often resisted.

First, we must recognize the tentative nature of knowledge. Our present understanding of science or of religion is likely, if it agrees with experience, to continue to have an important degree of validity just as does Newtonian mechanics. But there may be many deeper things which we do not yet know and which, when discovered, may modify our thinking in very basic ways.

EXPECTED PARADOXES

We must also expect paradoxes, and not be surprised or unduly troubled by them. We know of paradoxes in physics, such as that concerning the nature of light, which have been resolved by deeper understanding. We know of some which are still unresolved. In the realm of religion, we are troubled by the suffering around us and its apparent inconsistency with a God of love. Such paradoxes confronting science do not usually destroy our faith in science. They simply remind us of a limited understanding, and at times provide a key to learning more.

Perhaps there will be in the realm of religion cases of the uncertainty principle, which we now know is such a characteristic phenomenon of physics. If it is fundamentally impossible to determine accurately both the position and velocity of a particle, it should not surprise us if similar limitations occur in other aspects of our experience. This opposition in the precise determination of two quantities is also referred to as complementarity; position and velocity represent complementary aspects of a particle, only one of which can be measured at any one time.

Nils Bohr has already suggested that perception of man, or any living organism as a whole, and of his physical constitution represents this kind of complementarity. That is, the precise and close examination of the atomic makeup of man may of necessity blur our view of him as a living and spiritual being. In any case, there seems to be no justification for the dogmatic position taken by some that the remarkable phenomenon of individual human personality can be expressed completely in terms of the presently known laws of behavior of atoms and molecules. Justice and love may also represent such complementarity. A completely loving approach and the simultaneous meting out of exact justice hardly seem consistent.

These examples could only be somewhat fuzzy analogies of complementarity as it is known in science, or they may indeed be valid though still poorly defined occurrences of the uncertainty principle. But in any case, we should expect such occurrences and be forewarned by science that there will be fundamental limitations to our knowing everything at once with precision and consistency.

CONVERGE THEY MUST

Finally, if science and religion are so broadly similar, and not arbitrarily limited in their domain, they should at some time clearly converge. I believe this confluence is inevitable. For they both represent man's efforts to understand his universe and must ultimately be dealing with the same substance. As we understand more in each realm, the two must grow together. Perhaps by the time this convergence occurs, science will have been through a number of revolutions as striking as those which have occurred in the last century, and taken on a character not readily recognizable by scientists of today. Perhaps our religious understanding will also have seen progress and change. But converge they must, and through this should come new strength for both.

In the meantime, with only tentative understanding and in the face of uncertainty and change, how can we live gloriously and act decisively? It is this problem, I suspect, which has so often tempted man to insist that he has final and ultimate truth locked in some particular phraseology or symbolism, even when the phraseology may mean a hundred different things to a hundred different people. How well we can commit our lives to ideas which we recognize in principle as only tentative represents a real test of mind and emotions.

Galileo espoused the cause of Copernicus' theory of the solar system, and at great personal cost because of the Church's opposition. We know today that the question on which Galileo took his stand, the correctness of the idea that the earth rotates around the sun rather than the sun around the earth, is largely an unnecessary question. The two descriptions are equivalent, according to general relativity, although the first is simpler. And yet we honor Galileo for his pioneering courage and determination in deciding what he really thought was right and speaking out. This was important to his own integrity and to the development of the scientific and religious views of the time, out of which has grown our present better understanding of the problems he faced.

The authority of religion seemed more crucial in Galileo's Italy than it usually does today, and science more fresh and simple. We tend to think of ourselves as now more sophisticated, and science and religion as both more complicated so that our position can be less clear-cut. Yet if we accept the assumption of either one, that truth exists, surely each of us should undertake the same kind of task as did Galileo, or long before him, Gautama. For ourselves and for mankind, we must use our best wisdom and instincts, the evidence of history and wisdom of the ages, the experience and revelations of our friends, saints, and heroes in order to get as close as possible to truth and meaning. Furthermore, we must be willing to live and act on our conclusions.

Try These Projects For—
THE CONVERGENCE OF SCIENCE AND RELIGION,
by Townes

---

1. *Interviews.*

■ Draw up a list of questions you'd like to ask one or more of these people—a leading member of your congregation who is a scientist, your rabbi, a science teacher, a leading member of your congregation who is not a scientist, a Christian minister, parents, a college student.

■ Conduct as many interviews as you can, asking everybody the same questions.

■ Tape record the interviews, editing them if you can so that you can play back everyone's answer to your first question, then everyone's answer to the next question, and so on.

■ Take notes on the answers you get, then list all answers you get for one question, then all answers for another question, and so on.

■ Draw some conclusions, first about how each question was answered, and then about how each person handled all the questions. (Reminder: "Conclusions" includes new questions raised in your mind.)

■ Report, orally or in writing, on what you did, whom you asked and what questions, and what conclusions you came to, including your own new questions.

■ Make your tape or notes available to any students or the instructor if they want to examine the actual answers you got.

2. *Sight and sound.*

Ask the instructor about a list of filmstrips, films, recordings, tapes, and other aids for this unit, and where to get them.

■ With your instructor's help, select one and screen or play it.

■ Make notes on answers it gives to questions the group is presently discussing, new questions raised, new ideas you get, and so on. (You may have to replay your tapes several times for good notes.)

■ Report on your project and your notes, orally or in writing, mentioning only those points that have not already come up in class or in the essay.

■ Give your instructor your opinion on whether or not this audio-visual aid should be presented to the entire group, and if so whether in full or only certain parts. If your instructor knows the item, he can immediately agree with you or not. If he doesn't, give him your reasons and he'll decide from those. If the aid is presented to the class, you explain and interpret it.

3. *Teaching to learn.*

The Talmud tells us that no matter how much you may learn from your teachers and your classmates, you can learn even more from your own students. To test out this idea:

■ Select a younger person—your own brother or sister, or a friend's, or a younger pupil in the religious school.

■ Make notes on how you will explain to him any idea you want to about science or about religion or about both together. (What can you use besides words? Things he can see, hear, touch, do?)

■ Sit down with the younger person and teach him—talk to him, answer his questions, ask him your questions, show him things, take him places, or whatever. (Set yourself a definite time limit, and try in the last few minutes to check up on whether or not he's actually grasped the idea you had in mind.)

■ Make notes of his questions, your questions he couldn't answer, important points he didn't get, and especially his personal reactions—enjoyment, boredom, curiosity, appreciation, resentment.

■ Report your project, orally or in writing, telling what you did and giving a few examples of where you think you succeeded as a teacher, and a few where you think you failed; your fellow students—or your instructor—may have some suggestions for you about the failures.

4. *Express yourself.*

If you have a special talent, skill, hobby, or interest, put it to work for this essay and combine learning and pleasure. You might:

■ Write an original story, editorial, essay, poem, playlet.

■ Illustrate, draw, sketch, make a poster, cartoon, design.

■ Compose a prayer, song, dance, create a worship service.

■ Find and collect already published stories, editorials, essays, poems, playlets, drawings, posters, cartoons, prayers, songs about science, religion, and Judaism in any combination. Ask the students and instructor for suggestions on where to publish or exhibit or perform what you have created or collected.

5. *Research.*

Look into any of the following topics. Consult your instructor as to if, when, and how you should give a report.

■ Reactions of religious thinkers and institutions to the nineteenth-century developments in science. (Resources: *Encyclopaedia Brittanica;* I. G. Barbour, *Science and Religion.*)

■ Science innovators like Galileo, Newton, Harvey, Descartes, Pascal, Bacon. (Resources: H. Butterfield, *Origins of Modern Science;* J. Randall, *The Making of the Modern Mind.*)

■ Examples of scientific discovery by a "leap" of intuition. (Resource: J. Watson, *The Double Helix.*)

AFTER YOU HAVE READ—
THE CONVERGENCE OF SCIENCE AND RELIGION,
by Townes

Discuss these questions:

1. We are often told that science deals with the "how" of life and religion with the "why." Do you agree or disagree with this distinction? Support your answer with specific examples.

2. Certain aspects of religion and science may make them seem almost completely opposed to each other. What does Townes mean by (a) "difference in language used for historical reasons," and (b) "quantitative difference"?

3. The author compares the validity of the theory of gravity with the validity of religious ideas. Is this legitimate? Are gravity and religious ideas similar kinds of "theories"? Are the experiences of gravity and religion similar?

4. Do religion and science both represent man's efforts to understand his universe? Does religion include more than such efforts? Is Townes' assumed definition of religion inadequate? If not, is his conclusion about the "convergence of science and religion" valid?

5. Scientific discoveries like those of Copernicus, Galileo, Pasteur, Darwin, and others have often been a threat to absolutist religious doctrines in Christianity. Are there scientific theories, concepts, or discoveries today that threaten Judaism in any way? If so, do they threaten liberal Judaism (Reform, Conservative, modern Orthodox) as well as absolutist Judaism (strict Orthodox)?

6. We usually think of a religion as requiring commitment, devotion, allegiance. Can a religious person have these qualities if he accepts the idea that all beliefs are tentative, uncertain, "on trial"? If a scientist can live with uncertainty about his theories, why cannot a religionist live with uncertainty about his theories? On the other hand, are there some basic principles that a scientist accepts as absolutely certain—requiring his commitment, devotion, allegiance? Are there, in both science and religion, two different kinds of theories or beliefs—those we must feel certain of, and those we should feel uncertain of?

7. Townes, in his very first sentence, assumes that the "success" of science has been "ever-increasing." What does he mean by "success"? Do you agree with his concept of success? Either by his concept or by yours, has science really been successful? Do its successes outweigh any harms it has also done? Has religion been more of a "success" or more of a "failure" than science? Or do "success" and "failure" mean different things when you talk of religion as compared with talking about science?

8. Einstein had an abiding confidence in the order of the universe. As he put it, "The Lord God doesn't throw dice." Was this confidence based on a feeling, belief, faith, theory, hypothesis, experiments, facts, evidence, proof, or a combination of any of these? According to your answer, would you say Einstein was a religious man? Why or why not?

9. According to Townes, where does a scientist get his faith in an orderly universe? Is it a conclusion he draws from observation of facts? Or is it presupposition? What does Townes mean when he calls this faith "so deeply rooted" in the scientist? One way to test the source of scientific faith is to ask what would happen if the scientist finds disorder. Does he then give up his faith, because he is drawing conclusions only from observed facts? Or does he follow his innate belief or instinct, and decide he has not observed the facts correctly, or has not observed enough of them, or does not understand well enough what he has observed? Apply the same challenge to a religious person—Where does he get his faith in an orderly universe? How would he respond to disorder in the universe? Are the scientist and the religionist basically the same or basically different in their faith in an orderly universe? Perhaps this quotation from Einstein can help you clarify your thinking on these points: "To know that what is impenetrable to us really exists, manifesting itself as the highest wisdom and the most radiant beauty, which our dull faculties can comprehend only in their most primitive form . . . this knowledge, this feeling is at the center of true religiousness."

10. Go back over the "Before You Read" section for this essay. How would Townes answer these questions?

BEFORE YOU READ—

Ask yourself:

1. What is your own definition of science? Of religion?

2. Do your definitions conflict with each other, or are they compatible?

3. What is your own definition of knowledge? Of belief? Do you identify knowledge with science, and belief with religion? How would you distinguish between belief and superstition?

4. Does truth mean only what can be proved? Or are there truths that cannot be proved?

5. What do you mean by a miracle?

6. Do ends justify means? Does a good purpose excuse a wrong act?

7. What is your own definition of "the soul"? How does your definition relate to knowledge, belief, superstition, truth?

8. How do you react to this statement, "Since God is all-powerful, all-knowing, and all-good, man is not responsible for his own deeds, and God has no right to pass judgment on him"?

9. For you, what are the ultimate values or purposes of life?

SCIENCE AND RELIGION
Albert Einstein

Science and religion, if properly understood,
have important functions in man's fully real-
izing his potential rationality.

I

Duuring the last century, and part of the one before, it was widely held that there was an unreconcilable conflict between knowledge and belief. The opinion prevailed among advanced minds that it was time that belief should be replaced increasingly by knowledge; belief that did not itself rest on knowledge was superstition, and as such had to be opposed. According to this conception, the sole function of education was to open the way to thinking and knowing, and the school, as the outstanding organ for the people's education, must serve that end exclusively.

One will probably find but rarely, if at all, the rationalistic standpoint expressed in such crass form; for any sensible man would see at once how one-sided is such a statement of the position. But it is just as well to state a thesis starkly and nakedly, if one wants to clear up one's mind as to its nature.

It is true that convictions can best be supported with experience and clear thinking. On this point one must agree unreservedly with the extreme rationalist. The weak point of his conception is, however, this, that those convictions which are necessary and determinant for our conduct and judgments cannot be found solely along this solid scientific way.

For the scientific method can teach us nothing beyond how facts are related to, and conditioned by, each other. The aspiration toward such objective knowledge belongs to the highest of which man is capable, and you will certainly not suspect me of wishing to belittle the achievements and the heroic efforts of man in this sphere. Yet it is equally clear that knowledge of what *is* does not open the door directly to what *should be.* One can have the clearest and most complete knowledge of what *is,* and yet not be able to deduct from that what should be the *goal* of our human aspirations. Objective knowledge provides us with powerful instruments for the achievements of certain ends, but the ultimate goal itself and the longing to reach it must come from another source. And it is hardly necessary to argue for the view that our existence and our activity acquire meaning only by the setting up of such a goal and of corresponding values. The knowledge of truth as such is wonderful, but it is so little capable of acting as a guide that it cannot prove even the justification and the value of the aspiration toward that very knowledge of truth. Here we face, therefore, the limits of the purely rational conception of our existence.

But it must not be assumed that intelligent thinking can play no part in the formation of the goal and of ethical judgments. When someone realizes that for the achievement of an end certain means would be useful, the means itself becomes thereby an end. Intelligence makes clear to us the interrelation of means and ends. But mere thinking cannot give us a sense of the ultimate and fundamental ends. To make clear these fundamental ends and valuations, and to set them fast in the emotional life of the individual, seems to me precisely the most important function which religion has to perform in the social life of man. And if one asks whence derives the authority of such fundamental ends, since they cannot be stated and justified merely by reason, one can only answer: they exist in a healthy society as powerful traditions, which act upon the conduct and aspirations and judgments of the individuals; they are there, that is, as something living, without its being necessary to find justification for their existence. They come into being not through demonstration but through revelation, through the medium of powerful personalities. One must not attempt to justify them, but rather sense their nature simply and clearly.

The highest principles for our aspirations and judgment are given to us in the Jewish-Christian religious tradition. It is a very high goal which, with our weak powers, we can reach only very inadequately, but which gives a sure foundation to our aspirations and valuations. If one were to take that goal out of its religious form and look merely at its purely human side, one might state it perhaps thus: free and responsible development of the individual, so that he may place his powers freely and gladly in the service of all mankind.

There is no room in this for the divinization of a nation, or a class, let alone of an individual. Are we not all children of one father, as it is said in religious language? Indeed, even the divinization of humanity, as an abstract totality, would not be in the spirit of that ideal. It is only to the individual that a soul is given. And the high destiny of the individual is to serve rather than to rule, or to impose himself in any other way.

If one looks at the substance rather than at the form, then one can take these words as expressing also the fundamental democratic position. The true democrat can worship his nation as little as can the man who is religious, in our sense of the term.

What, then, in all this, is the function of education and of the school? They should help the young person to grow up in such a spirit that these fundamental principles should be to him as the air which he breathes. Teaching alone cannot do that.

If one holds these high principles clearly before one's eyes, and compares them with the life and spirit of our times, then it appears glaringly that civilized mankind finds itself at present in grave danger. In the totalitarian states it is the rulers themselves who strive actually to destroy that spirit of humanity. In less threatened parts it is nationalism and intolerance, as well as the oppression of the individuals by economic means, which threaten to choke these most precious traditions.

A realization of how great is the danger is spreading, however, among thinking people, and there is much search for means with which to meet the danger—means in the field of national and international politics, of legislation, or organization in general. Such efforts are, no doubt, greatly needed. Yet the ancients knew something which we seem to have forgotten. All means prove but a blunt instrument, if they have not behind them a living spirit. But if the longing for the achievement of the goal is powerfully alive within us, then shall we not lack the strength to find the means for reaching the goal and for translating it into deeds.

II

It would not be difficult to come to an agreement as to what we understand by science. Science is the century-old endeavor to bring together by means of systematic thought the perceptible phenomena of this world into as thorough-going an association as possible. To put it boldly, it is the attempt at the posterior reconstruction of existence by the process of conceptualization. But when asking myself what religion is I cannot think of the answer so easily. And even after finding an answer which may satisfy me at this particular moment, I still remain convinced that I can never under any circumstances bring together, even to a slight extent, the thoughts of all those who have given this question serious consideration.

At first, then, instead of asking what religion is I should prefer to ask what characterizes the aspirations of a person who gives me the impression of being religious: a person who is religiously enlightened appears to me to be one who has, to the best of his ability, liberated himself from the fetters of his selfish desires and is preoccupied with thoughts, feelings, and aspirations to which he clings because of their superpersonal value. It seems to me that what is important is the force of this superpersonal content and the depth of the conviction concerning its overpowering meaningfulness, regardless of whether any attempt is made to unite this content with a Divine Being, for otherwise it would not be possible to count Buddha and Spinoza as religious personalities. Accordingly, a religious person is devout in the sense that he has no doubt of the significance and loftiness of those superpersonal objects and goals which neither require nor are capable of rational foundation. They exist with the same necessity and matter-of-factness as he himself. In this sense religion is the age-old endeavor of mankind to become clearly and completely conscious of these values and goals and constantly to strengthen and extend their effect. If one conceives of religion and science according to these definitions then a conflict between them appears impossible. For science can only ascertain what *is*, but not what *should be*, and outside of its domain value judgments of all kinds remain necessary. Religion, on the other hand, deals only with evaluations of human thought and action: it cannot justifiably speak of facts and relationships between facts. According to this interpretation the well-known conflicts between religion and science in the past must all be ascribed to a misapprehension of the situation which has been described.

For example, a conflict arises when a religious community insists on the absolute truthfulness of all statements recorded in the Bible. This means an intervention on the part of religion into the sphere of science; this is where the struggle of the Church against the doctrines of Galileo and Darwin belongs. On

22

the other hand, representatives of science have often made an attempt to arrive at fundamental judgments with respect to values and ends on the basis of scientific method, and in this way have set themselves in opposition to religion. These conflicts have all sprung from fatal errors.

Now, even though the realms of religion and science in themselves are clearly marked off from each other, nevertheless there exist between the two strong reciprocal relationships and dependencies. Though religion may be that which determines the goal, it has, nevertheless, learned from science, in the broadest sense, what means will contribute to the attainment of the goals it has set up. But science can only be created by those who are thoroughly imbued with the aspiration toward truth and understanding. This source of feeling, however, springs from the sphere of religion. To this there also belongs the faith in the possibility that the regulations valid for the world of existence are rational, that is, comprehensible to reason. I cannot conceive of a genuine scientist without that profound faith. The situation may be expressed by an image: science without religion is lame, religion without science is blind.

Though I have asserted above that in truth a legitimate conflict between religion and science cannot exist, I must nevertheless qualify this assertion once again on an essential point, with reference to the actual content of historical religions. This qualification has to do with the concept of God. During the youthful period of mankind's spiritual evolution human fantasy created gods in man's own image, who, by the operations of their will, were supposed to determine, or at any rate to influence, the phenomenal world. Man sought to alter the disposition of these gods in his own favor by means of magic and prayer. The idea of God in the religions taught at present is a sublimation of that old concept of the gods. Its anthropomorphic character is shown, for instance, by the fact that men appeal to the Divine Being in prayers and plead for the fulfillment of their wishes.

Nobody, certainly, will deny that the idea of the existence of an omnipotent, just, and omnibeneficent personal God is able to accord man solace, help, and guidance; also, by virtue of its simplicity it is accessible to the most undeveloped mind. But, on the other hand, there are decisive weaknesses attached to this idea in itself, which have been painfully felt since the beginning of history. That is, if this Being is omnipotent, then every occurrence, including every human action, every human thought, and every human feeling and aspiration is also His work; how is it possible to think of holding men responsible for their deeds and thoughts before such an almighty Being? In giving out punishment and rewards He would to a certain extent be passing judgment on Himself. How can this be combined with the goodness and righteousness ascribed to Him?

The main source of the present-day conflicts between the spheres of religion and of science lies in this concept of a personal God. It is the aim of science to establish general rules which determine the reciprocal connection of objects and events in time and space. For these rules, or laws of nature, absolutely general validity is required—not proven. It is mainly a program, and faith in the possibility of its accomplishment in principle is only founded on partial successes. But hardly anyone could be found who would deny these partial successes and ascribe them to human self-deception. The fact that on the basis of such laws we are able to predict the temporal behavior of phenomena in certain domains with great precision and certainty is deeply embedded in the consciousness of the modern man, even though he may have grasped very little of the contents of those laws. He need only consider that planetary courses within the solar system may be calculated in advance with great exactitude on the basis of a limited number of simple laws. In a similar way, though not with the same precision, it is possible to calculate in advance the mode of operation of an electric motor, a transmission system, or of a wireless apparatus, even when dealing with a novel development.

To be sure, when the number of factors coming into play in a phenomenological complex is too large, scientific method in most cases fails us. One need only think of the weather, in which case prediction even for a few days ahead is impossible. Nevertheless, no one doubts that we are confronted with a causal connection whose causal components are in the main known to us. Occurrences in this domain are beyond the reach of exact prediction because of the variety of factors in operation, not because of any lack of order in nature.

We have penetrated far less deeply into the regularities obtaining within the realm of living things, but deeply enough nevertheless to sense at least the rule of fixed necessity. One need only think of the systematic order in heredity and in the effect of poisons, as for instance alcohol, on the behavior of organic beings. What is still lacking here is a grasp of connections of profound generality, but not a knowledge of order in itself.

The more a man is imbued with the ordered regularity of all events the firmer becomes his conviction that there is no room left by the side of this ordered regularity for causes of a different nature. For him neither the rule of human nor the rule of divine will exist as an independent cause of natural events. To be sure, the doctrine of a personal God interfering with natural events could never be *refuted*, in the real sense, by science, for this doctrine can always take refuge in those domains in which scientific knowledge has not yet been able to set foot.

But I am persuaded that such behavior on the part of the representatives of religion would not only be unworthy but also fatal. For a doctrine which is able to maintain itself not in clear light but only in the dark will of necessity lose its effect on mankind, with incalculable harm to human progress. In their struggle for the ethical good, teachers of religion must have the stature to give up the doctrine of a personal God, that is, give up that source of fear and hope which in the past placed such vast power in the hands of priests. In their labors they will have to avail themselves of those forces which are capable of cultivating the Good, the True, and the Beautiful in humanity itself. This is, to be sure, a more difficult but an incomparably more worthy task.* After religious leaders accomplish the refining process indicated they will surely recognize with joy that true religion has been ennobled and made more profound by scientific knowledge.

If it is one of the goals of religion to liberate mankind as far as possible from the bondage of egocentric cravings, desires, and fears, scientific reasoning can aid religion in another sense. Although it is true that it is the goal of science to discover rules which permit the association and foretelling of facts, this is not its only aim. It also seeks to reduce the connections discovered to the smallest possible number of mutually independent conceptual elements. It is in this striving after the rational unification of the manifold that it encounters its greatest successes, even though it is precisely this attempt which causes it to run the greatest risk of falling a prey to illusions. But whoever has undergone the intense experience of successful advances made in this domain is moved by profound reverence for the rationality made manifest in existence. By way of the understanding he achieves a far-reaching emancipation from the shackles of personal hopes and desires, and thereby attains that humble attitude of mind toward the grandeur of reason incarnate in existence, and which, in its profoundest depths, is inaccessible to man. This attitude, however, appears to me to be religious, in the highest sense of the word. And so it seems to me that science not only purifies the religious impulse of the dross of its anthropomorphism but also contributes to a religious spiritualization of our understanding of life.

The further the spiritual evolution of mankind advances, the more certain it seems to me that the path to genuine religiosity does not lie through the fear of life, and the fear of death, and blind faith, but through striving after rational knowledge. In this sense I believe that the priest must become a teacher if he wishes to do justice to his lofty educational mission.

---

* This thought is convincingly presented in Herbert Samuel's book, *Belief and Action*.

TRY THESE PROJECTS FOR—
SCIENCE AND RELIGION,
by Einstein

---

1. *What I know and what I believe.*

A large poster for the wall or bulletin board. (If you want to involve a committee or the whole class, change "I" to "we.") Make up a list of statements for the items below, in two columns headed "I know that" and "I believe that":

I know that	Item	I believe that
_____	1. The Bible _____	
_____	2. God _____	
_____	3. The law of gravity _____	
_____	4. Religion _____	
_____	5. Israel _____	
_____	6. Space travel _____	
_____	7. Life after death _____	
_____	8. The future _____	
_____	9. Worship _____	
_____	10. Science _____	
_____	11. My family _____	
_____	12. My synagogue _____	

Add or substitute any items you want to, of course—and write "I don't know" or "I don't believe" wherever you prefer. Be ready to answer questions from students or instructor like "How do you know that?" or "Why do you believe that?"

2. *Express yourself.*

Write a prayer, in which you do not ask God to do something or give you something, but ask God to help you do or give something (not get something). Be very specific about what it is God is to help you do or give—nothing vague or general. You may prefer to imagine you are someone else—a teacher, a lawyer, a draft dodger, a prisoner in jail, a world statesman, a rabbi, a scientist, or whatever, and write such a prayer for him. Or, you may prefer to write the prayer for a group—your family, the American people, Israel, Russian Jews, a black community, etc.

■ Write a letter to Townes or Einstein or any other scientist, in which you agree with him on certain specific points (no vague generalities), or disagree with him (ditto). Try to get your letter published somewhere, as "An Open Letter to. . . " If the scientist is alive today, send your letter to him, and publish his reply along with your letter.

■ Imagine a dialogue between Townes (or Einstein or any other scientist) and a great religious leader like Moses, a prophet, a talmudic rabbi, Maimonides, a noted modern rabbi. Look over the questions that precede and follow the two essays, so far, and pick just one of them for your imaginary dialogue. After your dialogue is completed, have it checked out by the instructor, a friend, students, parents. Revise it if necessary, then get it published somewhere, or put it on tape with a friend, or act it out for the class, an assembly, a parents' meeting, etc.

■ Select a poem about religion, science, or mathematics (from those reprinted in this unit and others in books like *Imagination's Other Place*, edited by Helen Plotz) and prepare to give it a dramatic reading, memorized or from the book, on tape, to the class, an assembly, a meeting, an adult class, a faculty meeting, etc.

3. *Sketch some lively cartoons.*

Look through the two essays so far and their questions and projects, and think up some bright ideas. For example: A man standing on global earth, saying, "Of course it's flat—anybody can see that." A man shutting his eyes tight and saying, "My mind's made up, so don't confuse me with the facts." "God" with a long white beard sitting on a throne in the sky filling "orders" that people "pray" up to Him. Or "God" as a cosmic bellhop—we push buttons and He comes running to see what we want. A man stealing or committing some other crime, and saying, "I have to do this—it's a matter of fixed necessity."

4. *Sociodrama.*

You are a group of Israeli government leaders some time in the future. Russia (as she did to Finland and Czechoslovakia) is about to invade Israel, for some reason or other—it doesn't matter. Argue out your alternatives. Fight back? (What are the possible outcomes?) Give in? (What is the balance between what you might "save" and what you might "lose"?) Other alternatives? (For each, what possible outcomes, what balance between "save" and "lose"?) Remember: As Israeli leaders you know Jewish history well, especially the Jewish revolt against Rome in 67 C.E., when the Jewish people faced the very same situation and the very same alternatives, and made their decision.

So, better look up the conflicting attitudes among Jewish leaders and groups on that revolt: the "hawks" who said fight to the death for complete political independence; and the "doves" who said surrender political freedom, pay taxes, etc., in order to preserve Jewish religion, culture, schools, synagogues, and as much religious and cultural independence as possible. Draw parallels, after investigating these attitudes, with the Russian takeover of Czechoslovakia and the probable attitude of Israelis should a great power try to take them over. Be ready to bring your historical information and your parallels to bear on an argument over "ends and means—does one justify the other?" Does history repeat itself? And can we learn anything from history? Or is it always "an entirely new ball game"?

Set yourself a time limit, and leave exactly one minute for a final, irrevocable "vote." Afterward, if you like, discuss your "discussion": Did science play a part in your arguments? Did religion? Did history? Did a concept of purpose in being a Jewish state? Did concepts of God, fate, destiny, reward, punishment?

5. *Research.*

Look into any of these topics. Consult the instructor as to if, when, and how you should give a report.

■ Epistemology (the study or theory of knowledge, the validity, and its limits).

■ Superstition—meaning, history, the Jewish attitude (as in the *Union Prayer Book* I, 71).

■ Magic (not the stage kind; the "real" kind).

■ Basic religious ideas of Buddha and/or Spinoza (who did not believe in a "Divine Being") as compared with those of a Jewish religious naturalist. (Resources: Any standard encyclopedia or history of religion; Roland B. Gittelsohn, "The God We Worship: A Naturalist View," in *Dimensions in American Judaism,* Fall, 1967; also by Gittelsohn, *Wings of the Morning.*)

AFTER YOU HAVE READ—
SCIENCE AND RELIGION,
by Einstein

Discuss these questions:

1. Einstein's definitions of science and religion (below)—How do they compare with your own? Are they conflicting or compatible? Does one "endeavor" help or hinder the other, and how? Which definition seems to have been harder for him to frame than the other, and why?

   science: ". . .the century-old endeavor to bring together by means of systematic thought the perceptible phenomena of this world into as thoroughgoing an association as possible."

   religion: ". . .the age-old endeavor of mankind to become clearly and completely conscious of (superpersonal) values and goals and constantly to strengthen and extend their effect."

   In other words, as he says elsewhere: science—the knowledge of what is; religion—the knowledge of what should be.

2. If you agree that science and religion do not conflict, but rather supplement each other, where then do so many people get the idea that they do conflict— that you must accept either one or the other, but cannot accept both.

3. Is knowledge ever superior to belief? Is belief ever superior to knowledge? Give specific examples, preferably from your own personal experience, to support your answers.

4. What kind of knowledge is referred to in the following statement from midrashic literature? Why did sages rate it so valuable and important?

   "If you have acquired knowledge, what do you lack? If you lack knowledge, what do you have?" (*Ecclesiastes Rabbah* to 7.23)

5. In Jewish life and thought, knowledge has always been considered vital. Yet in the familiar Bible story, God forbids Adam and Eve to eat from the Tree of Knowledge. How would you explain the discrepancy? (Don't say it's just a meaningless, superstitious old "myth"—our wisest and most learned ancestors included it in sacred scripture, studied it, taught it, commented on it, interpreted it.) Hints: Is knowledge ever dangerous? Are there right and wrong ways to gain it? Is knowledge an absolute "value" or does it depend on who has it, how he got it, what he uses it for?

6. Einstein says superstition is belief that does not rest on knowledge. Scheffler, a modern philosopher, makes these three interesting statements about knowledge and belief. Does he agree or disagree with Einstein?

"Believing aims at the truth, while knowing succeeds in this aim."

"We ask, How do you know? and Why do you believe? but not vice versa."

"Knowing, unlike believing, has independent factual reference."

(Israel Scheffler, *Conditions of Knowledge.*)

7. What is an "ethical truth"? Give specific examples, preferably from your own personal experience. Can an ethical truth be "proved"? If not, does that make it inferior to factual truth?

8. First, consider these passages from Jewish literature. Then from them, determine the Jewish concept of truth. Finally, decide whether Einstein accepts this concept.

"The truth of the Lord endures forever." (Psalms 118:2)

"The seal of the Holy One is truth." (*Talmud Shabbat* 55a)

"A truth established by proof neither gains force or certainty by the consent of all scholars, nor less by general dissent." (Maimonides, *Guide,* 2.15)

"Truth can stand, falsehood cannot." (*Talmud Shabbat* 104a)

"O Lord, open our eyes that we may see and welcome all truth, whether shining from the annals of ancient revelations or reaching us through the seers of our own time." (*Union Prayer Book*, I, 34)

9. Does Einstein express a Jewish position when he says, ". . . knowledge of what *is* does not open the door directly to what *should be*"? Do you agree with him?

10. Go back over the "Before You Read" section for this essay. How would Einstein answer these questions?

Graffiti on a washroom wall at M.I.T.:

And God said

$$\frac{mv^2}{r} = \frac{Ze^2}{r^2}$$

$$mvr = n\frac{h}{2\pi}$$

$$r = \frac{r^2h^2}{(2\pi)^2mZe^2}$$

$$E = \frac{1}{2}mv^2 - \frac{Ze^2}{r}$$

$$E = \frac{2\pi^2mZ^2e^4}{n^2h^2} = R_y$$

and there was light.

Before You Read—

SCIENCE
AND
CREATION,
by Etkin

Label the following statements TRUE or FALSE:

_____ 1. The story of creation in Genesis, Chapter 1, is not acceptable to modern science.

_____ 2. The theory of evolution explains how everything in the world today—including human character, intellect, and belief—came to be as it is.

_____ 3. According to scientists, the universe in the past has always developed from some previous condition.

_____ 4. Man's higher intellectual abilities—language, mathematics, and so on—as well as his religious and ethical attitudes evolved in the same way as his physical structure and abilities: gradually, and because they were factors promoting survival.

_____ 5. The origin of life traces back to known physical and chemical processes.

_____ 6. There never was, is, or will be "anything new under the sun."

_____ 7. Scientific knowledge can help us decide whether or not the universe has a purpose.

_____ 8. All scientists agree that evolution has no direct motive or purpose, but is entirely a phenomenon of chance and statistics.

SCIENCE AND CREATION
William Etkin

Is science really able to deal with the problem
of creation? What do recent scientific findings
illustrate about the nature of creation?

Oಮ NE OF THE CLEAR-CUT distinctions between religious thought and that of natural science has always seemed to be the acceptance of an act of creation by religion and not by science.[1] The very basis of the mechanism characteristic of scientific thought appears to be an infinite regression from effect to cause, then to cause of that cause and so on *ad infinitum*. In natural science we have become accustomed to thinking of origin by evolution from previous conditions, never of a genuine act of creation, never of the origin of anything really new. The concept of evolution, central in modern science, is often accepted as a denial of the concept of creation.

Yet an examination of current theories in astronomy and biology raises many doubts as to the validity of the idea of necessary conflict between the concepts of evolution and creation. In astronomy the advent of nuclear physics has brought with it a reaffirmation of the possibility of creation. One group of current theories, indeed, derives the known universe from an initial explosion concentrated in time and space, an act of creation as clear and simple as a command from the Lord. And in biology a leading current speculation, the notion of emergent evolution, is nothing but the concept of creation thinly disguised as mechanism. Let us ask to what extent these ideas, now at least respectable if not universally accepted by the more philosophical among scientists, indicate a convergence of scientific and religious thinking on this issue.

In 1952, George Gamow, professor of physics at George Washington University and a leading American atomic physicist, published a book called *The Creation of the Universe*.[2] In it Gamow gave a popular presentation of a theory which he and others had expounded on several occasions previously in scientific circles. Recently the theory has been brought up to date in an article in the *Scientific American* for March, 1954.[3] In his theory Gamow uses two widely accepted and basic concepts in modern cosmology. These are the idea of the expanding universe and the notion that all the major features of our universe are of limited age, something in the neighborhood of three to five billion years. Gamow's major contribution is the particular explanation in terms of modern atomic physics of the course of cosmic evolution.

The notion of the expanding universe goes back to the 1920s when the American astronomer, Hubble, discovered that certain faint star-like objects in

---

1. A perusal of Isaac Husik's *A History of Mediaeval Jewish Philosophy* reveals the central place occupied in the philosophic thought of that time by the problem of creation. The attempt to understand rabbinic Judaism in terms of the science of the times (Aristotelian philosophy) stimulated a broadening and deepening of our understanding of the tradition. Today we feel pressed by more material conflicts or perhaps we do not possess a mind, like Maimonides, at home in both areas. At any rate it is in the hope of stimulating a cooperative exchange of ideas that this analysis of modern scientific thinking on this issue is offered.

2. G. Gamow, *The Creation of the Universe*, Viking Press, N.Y. 1952.

3. G. Gamow, "Modern Cosmology," *Scientific American*, v. 190 pp. 55–63, 1954.

the heavens are not really single stars but whole galaxies with millions of stars in each. These universes are so distant that in ordinary telescopes the individual stars cannot be distinguished. It had been known previously that the light from these objects showed a peculiar shift of the lines in their spectrum, the so-called red shift. This shift indicates that the galaxies are receding from us at tremendous speeds. When the true distance of these galaxies was appreciated through Hubble's work the differences in red shift among the galaxies were seen to form a consistent and amazing pattern. The further out in space they are the faster they are receding from us. For each million light years away (a light year is equal to about six thousand billion miles) the speed of recession increases by about 100 miles per second. It is as though the universe is expanding like the products of a great explosion.

If we were to examine a photograph taken a fraction of a second after an explosion of a hand grenade we would see some particles further from the center of the explosion than others. The degree of blurring of the picture due to the movement of the particles would enable us to measure the speed of each particle just as the red shift in starlight tells us how fast each star is receding from us. We would then find that the speed of the farther objects was greater than that of those nearer the center. This is necessarily so since all pieces started from the point of explosion at the same time and their scattering resulted from differences in force and direction acting on each. It would not be difficult by determining the speed, position, and direction of the particles on the photograph to localize the time and place of the original grenade explosion.

The picture of the expanding universe drawn by astronomers is similar to such a photograph except that, for reasons we cannot go into, the location of the center is not indicated. What Gamow did is to calculate back from the speed and position of the expanding fragments (the galaxies) to an original time of explosion. The answer he comes to is the recurrent theme of all modern calculations of the age of major features of the universe, a few billion years. The original estimates were somewhat more than two billion years but recent checks, using the results of photographs with the new 200 inch telescope, have more than doubled that figure.

The second aspect of Gamow's theory borrowed from standard conclusions of contemporary science is that which fixes the age of the earth, the moon, planets, and the very matter of the universe at again that intriguing figure, a few billion years. Without attempting to go into detail we may briefly consider the evidence on each of these scores.

The dating of the oldest rocks of our earth's crust has been given precision by modern atomic theory. The rate of radioactive decay of uranium to one kind (isotope) of lead is known accurately. With this knowledge the age of uranium-containing rocks can be estimated by determining the ratio of uranium to lead in them. Such rocks, the oldest on the earth's surface, again turn up our magic number—a few billion years.

Astronomers have long suspected that the moon originated by splitting off from the earth. One theory has it that the great Pacific basin represents the scar left by this cosmic fission. Everyone knows that the gravitational pull of the moon on the earth produces the tides. But few realize two factors that accompany these tidal effects, the slowing down of the rotation of the earth and the recession of the moon from the earth. At present the slowing down of the rotation of the earth is lengthening the day by one thousandth of a second per century and causing the moon to move farther from the earth by some five inches per year. Appropriate calculations carry us back to the time the moon was in contact with the earth's surface. Then the earth spun round on its axis in about seven hours. The date—again our magic figure—a few billion years.

Many other characteristics of our universe, such as the proportion of radioactive isotopes, the age of the sea judged on the basis of its salt content, the life cycle of the stars all point to the same magic number—a few billion years—as the date when they all began. Since many quantitative uncertainties accompany these calculations the variation around four to six billion years given by different methods may be regarded as secondary. The primary point is that all the evidence points to a time of beginning for all things, about five billion years ago.

How does Gamow envisage the possible origin of the universe at the zero hour? At that time all matter and energy was concentrated together in one small area— but let us permit Gamow to speak for himself: "The nearest guess is that the overall density of the universe at that time was comparable to that of nuclear fluid, tiny droplets of which form the nuclei of various atoms. This would make the original preexplosion density of the universe a hundred thousand billion times greater than the density of water; each cubic centimeter of space contained at that time a hundred million tons of matter"! (A cubic inch is equal to about 17 cubic centimeters.) To this central nuclear pulp from which he conceives the universe to have arisen Gamow has given the name Ylem (i lem). In modern physics matter and energy are interchangeable. Gamow's Ylem is calculated to consist more largely of intense radiant energy than matter, with a resulting temperature of some 15 billion degrees. This original Ylem started expanding with explosive violence and as its volume increased energy was converted to matter. The temperature fell and different kinds of atoms of ordinary matter appeared. In only about one hour most of the different kinds of atoms of our world had appeared. In the next 30 million years the temperature fell to a few thousand degrees until the atoms of gas condensed to form vast clouds of gas-dust. It is by condensation of these clouds that all the stars and nebulae of our universe were formed. We will not go further into Gamow's fascinating story because it is beyond our present interest. The main point for us is clear. Some scientists by the ordinary process of science, the analysis of evidence, are led to the conclusion that the universe had a definite beginning. From then its main physical features were laid down in a relatively short time.

Of course this theory of Gamow's, though it is representative of what appears to be the leading mode of current speculation among scientists as to the physical origin of the universe is not either universally accepted or without competing suggestions. Hoyle in his book *The Nature of the Universe*[4] describes a fascinating alternative conception developed by a group of British astronomers. This too is a type of creation theory. They conceive matter as arising spontaneously throughout the universe in the form of hydrogen atoms. This "continuous creation" as Hoyle calls it produces an extremely rarified interstellar gas whose condensations produce the stars. As a consequence of continuous creation the condensed masses move away from each other producing the phenomenon of the expansion of the universe. Despite this expansion, continuous new formation of matter keeps the number of galaxies in a given area constant. This bald summary may make this conception seem highly fanciful and in fact Hoyle does not deny the unconventionality of its outlook. But let us see in his own words how he defends it:

"Some people have argued that continuous creation introduces a new assumption into science—and a very startling assumption at that. Now I do not agree that continuous creation is an additional assumption. It is certainly a new hypothesis, but it only replaces a hypothesis that lies concealed in the older theories which assume, as I have said before, that the whole of the matter in the universe was created in one big bang at a particular time in the remote past."

Hoyle's claim for the advantages of the concept of continuous creation over the "big bang" idea though technical in detail can be summarized as follows. The results of today's observation of the universe are more easily and more consistently derived from the assumptions of continuous creation than from alternative theories. Even were it within our capacities here to evaluate these theories, it would be unnecessary. From our present point of view it is sufficient to notice that both types of theories contain the notion of creation—the origin of something without determinable antecedents, without causes in the mechanistic or scientific sense of that word. To my own mind, perhaps because of my education, the Gamow type of theory represents a possible "real"—therefore true—solution. Hoyle's seems to be merely a mathematical fiction—useful perhaps—but not real. However such metaphysical prejudices have nothing to do with our present thesis. It is clear that the fundamental notion of creativity is acceptable and indeed largely accepted in scientific astronomy.

Biology is certainly the stronghold among the sciences of the concept of evolution. It is therefore somewhat strange to find that the more philosophic of biologists of this century are much taken up by doctrines of emergence and wholes, doctrines which are in some respects supplementary but in others contradictory to the basic notion of evolution. The late William Morton Wheeler of Harvard[5]

---

4. F. Hoyle, *The Nature of the Universe*, Harper Bros., N.Y. 1950.

5. W. M. Wheeler, *Emergent Evolution and the Development of Societies*, W. W. Norton, N.Y. 1928.

and H. S. Jennings of Johns Hopkins[6] were leading American proponents who wrote using the term "emergent evolution" introduced by C. L. Morgan.[7] That versatile genius, Jan Smuts,[8] propounded similar doctrines under the name of Holism. Though not a professional biologist himself, Smuts' Holism won considerable support from biologists. And of course, many philosophers from the French Bergson[9] to the American Lovejoy[10] and the English Whitehead[11] have supported comparable ideas under various names. In more recent discussions by scientists the term "levels of integration" has been widely used as in A. C. Redfield's book,[12] a symposium with that title. "Organicism" is commonly used to refer to doctrines similar to Smuts' Holism by a number of biologists as J. S. Haldane 1914,[13] E. W. Sinnott[14] and Von Bertalanffy.[15]

Despite the variety of phrases used to describe these doctrines their fundamental notion is everywhere the same. In evolution new combinations and patternings of previously existing parts are produced. In these new patterns genuinely new qualities emerge, qualities not predictable from a knowledge of the component parts since these qualities are dependent upon relations not previously present. An often quoted example is the emergence of new properties when the gases oxygen and hydrogen are combined chemically to produce water. Living things are composed of the same matter and energy found in the inorganic world but because of the patterning of these parts in their new relationships in the living organism new properties appear. The basic notion of emergent evolution is that these new properties could not have been predicted merely from a knowledge of the physics and chemistry of the compounds involved. It is these new "emergent" properties which we call "life." Similarly we may suppose the mental to have arisen from the biological and the spiritual (if we can find, as it seems we can today, biologists who accept the reality of the spiritual) from the mental.

From one point of view these philosophies are an ingenious attempt to reconcile determinism with creation. It can be seen that creation is involved, for at each "level" of evolution new properties, not in any sense contained or limited by the nature of the old, have emerged. Something new has arisen whose nature is not predetermined by the old although it arises only in conjunction with and in

6. H. S. Jennings, *The Universe and Life*, Yale University Press, New Haven, 1933.

7. C. L. Morgan, *Emergent Evolution*, Henry Holt, N.Y. 1922.

8. J. C. Smuts, *Holism and Evolution*, Macmillan Co., N.Y., 1926.

9. H. Bergson, *Creative Evolution*, Henry Holt, N.Y., 1928.

10. A. O. Lovejoy, "The Meaning of Emergence and Its Modes," *Journal of Philosophic Studies* v. 2 pp. 167–187, 1927.

11. A. N. Whitehead, *Science and the Modern World*, Macmillan Co., N.Y., 1925.

12. Redfield, *Levels of Integration in Biological and Social Systems*, J. Cattell Press, Lancaster, Pa., 1942.

13. J. S. Haldane, *Mechanism, Life and Personality*, Dutton, N.Y., 1914.

14. E. W. Sinnott, *Cell and Psyche*, University of North Carolina Press, Chapel Hill, 1950.

15. L. Von Bertalanffy, *Problems of Life*, Wiley & Sons, N.Y., 1952.

consequence of new relations established among preexisting parts. In this sense emergent evolution and the various forms of organicism are not strictly mechanistic since they make of evolution something more than a mere unfolding of predetermined events. But at least on the descriptive level such concepts seem consistent with the theory of organic evolution since they call for no new creation of matter. It is in this sense that they are usually thought of by biologists. The fact is usually ignored that creativity with regard to the properties of the new wholes is clearly implied with a consequent breakdown in the rigidity of scientific determinism.

It is not our purpose here to subject the concepts relating to emergent evolution to critical analysis. That is a technical task better done elsewhere. But it may be said that, though such an analysis throws grave doubts upon the legitimacy of the application of the idea of emergence to the origin of life itself or to the lower stages of evolutionary change in organisms, it strangely strengthens the doctrine in respect to the origin of man's higher mental processes, his spiritual qualities, from the animal mind. For our purposes it will be sufficient to elaborate sufficiently on this last point to make it clear.

The evolutionist (and all contemporary scientific biologists are evolutionists) derives man's physical structure from that of a primate ape-like ancestry by gradual modification through natural selection. Each of these changes enabled the evolving human being to function more efficiently in relation to the particular mode of making a living which he followed. In some respects assumptions must be made about the manner of life of the ancestral forms at one stage and another in order to account for the advantages of a particular condition. Thus, it has been usual for biologists to assume that man's ancestors were once tree-living. Under such conditions we can see that certain of man's structural characteristics could well have developed because they would be advantageous there. Thus the evolution of a grasping hand with opposable thumb and of eyes capable of binocular vision permitting accurate judgment of distance are readily accounted for in such an environment because each would there confer obvious advantages to its possessors. On the other hand, man's foot must have evolved later after the tree-living habit had been given up because the foot is adapted to progression on the ground. Similarly, many of the basic behavioral traits of man, male aggressiveness in defence of his group, mother love that lasts for years, etc., are plainly of selective value to their possessors. Such characteristics can be thought of as evolving by ordinary natural selection, a strictly mechanistic, cause-and-effect, process. The result is gradual and progressive. No new creative act is called for because, in a sense, the outcome was contained in the potentialities of the original. It is clear then that some of the basic behavioral traits of mankind can be accounted for on a purely naturalistic basis.[16]

---

16. W. Etkin, "Social Behavior and the Evolution of Man's Mental Faculties," *The American Naturalist*, v. 88 pp. 129–142, 1954.

Such evolutionary progression would produce a fine specimen of a man-like ape, but never a human being because by such gradual evolutionary progression man's highest mental capacities could never have arisen. Consider for example man's intellect. Some of its components are the capacity for abstraction, for the use of sounds to create complex language, for the elaborate handling of numbers and of quantitative concepts generally. These are not like the difference between man's hand and the hand of his primitive primate ancestor, merely one of degree of which all intermediate stages existed. In various monkeys and apes types of hands more as well as less specialized than man's exist. However as regards man's intelligence, this is not so. In the words of G. G. Simpson, mankind's intellect shows "what amounts to a difference in kind and not only a relative difference of degree."[17] Henry Nissen of the Yale laboratory of primate behavior writes: "With one notable exception the phylogentic course of behavioral development has been gradual, that it has been a continuous affair, proceeding by quantitative rather than qualitative changes, the one exception is that which marks the transition from the highest nonhuman primates to man. At this point a new 'dimension' or mode of development emerges; culture or 'social heredity.'"[18]

So much for the opinion of authorities. Let us look at the matter more directly. Consider for example, modern man's mathematical capacities, his handling of numbers and of geometrical reasoning. True, these have to be learned anew by each generation. Still, man and man alone, has the capacity for learning such number concepts. Some animals as crows appear to be able to distinguish two objects from three. One experimenter credits jackdaws with a number sense to six and a bright ape might go to ten when pushed. But the gulf between the characteristically human capacity for learning mathematical concepts and that of the animal is a wide and unbridged chasm.

Similarly with man's capacity for use of language. Many animals can rival man in his sound making capacities. Indeed some, like the parrot, can give a somewhat life-like imitation of his speech. But no serious student confuses "polly wants a cracker" with true human speech. Even the best trained apes can make only the barest beginnings of the use of speech to express needs or specific information. Years of training have produced nothing more than the use of a two or three word vocabulary. The psychologists from the Kelloggs[19] to the Hayes[20] who have attempted to teach apes to speak by raising them in the home like human babies have been compelled to the conclusion that the reason they do not learn to talk is because their mental capacities simply are not up to the task. It was a triumph

17. G. G. Simpson, *The Meaning of Evolution*, Yale University Press, New Haven, 1949.

18. H. W. Nissen, "Social Behavior in Primates," in C. Stone, *Comparative Psychology*, Prentice-Hall, N.Y., 1951.

19. W. N. Kellogg and L. A. Kellogg, *The Ape and the Child*, McGraw-Hill Book Co., N.Y., 1933.

20. C. Hayes, *The Ape in Our House*, Harper Bros., N.Y., 1950.

of two years of patient laborious teaching when Mrs. Hayes' chimpanzee finally reached the stage of saying "cup-cup" when very thirsty.

The mere fact that there is a gap between one animal type and others does not prove that the gap could not have been the product of gradual evolutionary change. The intermediate forms may simply have died out. Indeed, modern biology is replete with examples of such phenomena. Birds and reptiles are today separated by a clear-cut gap, yet we know many fossils that link the two and need not doubt that all intermediate stages once existed. Then what is so different about the isolation of man? Just this. Every intermediate step between reptile and bird was presumably an advantageous step. Since each advance conveyed some survival value on its possessor it was subject to natural selection. It therefore evolved by the usual evolutionary mechanisms.

But we cannot think of man's higher intellectual abilities, for example his mathematical and language abilities, as evolving in the same way. These are capacities never exercised as such in a state of nature. Accounts of primitive cultures often note that the practice of counting is often extremely limited, sometimes to only three. It must be presumed then that the number sense, since never used in its higher reaches by primitive man, could never have entered into the arena of natural selection. Its improvement could never have been subject to natural selection in the way that every slight improvement in the grasp of the hand or the accuracy of the eye was. Language sense, which comes into play only in its most rudimentary forms in primitive cultures despite their complex grammars could not have reached the heights seen in every flowering of culture if its development depended upon natural selection operating on precultural societies. Similarly with music and the plastic arts. And, I think, similarly with man's ethical sensibilities, although here the argument is more involved and would need separate treatment.

It is the existence of this gap between man's mentality and that of apes and the impossibility of bridging it by the usual mechanisms of evolution that furnishes the main drive behind the elaboration of theories of emergence. In terms of such theories the gap is not denied. It is not bridged. It is leaped over. The higher faculties are declared a new emergent that appears more or less suddenly, an incidental consequence of the evolution of the cerebral cortex. For example, Julian Huxley in a justly famous and influential essay called "The Uniqueness of Man" (1941) writes, "Although it (i.e., man's intelligence) has been brought about by the gradual quantitative enlargement of the association areas of the brain, the result has been almost as abrupt as the change (also brought about quantitatively) from solid ice to liquid water." Some biologists explicitly accept the emergent evolution explanation at this point, others use the terminology of emergent evolution as in the above quotation without explicit commitment to the philosophy behind it.

In falling back on emergent evolution, explicitly or implicitly, as an explanation of man's unique mental powers, biologists are in essence relying upon the concept of creation. The new qualities were not present or in any way determinable in the old parts. Therefore something not predictable, not deterministically fixed, has appeared from no antecedent. Here in the origin of man's higher mental capacities as in the origin of the physical universe current thinking not only allows but supports the introduction of the concept of creation.

Our factual conclusion is then that scientific theory today offers no mechanistic answer to two of the fundamental problems of human thought, the origin of the universe and the origin of man's soul. It tells us only that their origins cannot be explained today in the mechanistic manner in which science seeks to explain other phenomena. The concept of creation has to be introduced at these two points.

Of course in invoking creation, science does not distinguish as to whether the creation is the act of a purposeful creator or a mere random accident. It merely asserts that the study of mechanisms has run into a dead end in which the nonmechanistic notion of creation must be invoked. Science by its nature cannot study the character of a creation. For the business of natural science is the interpretation of evidence in terms of mechanistic cause and effect. Where the evidence leads to the concept of creation science may follow. But where the evidence stops it must stop. The concept of creation is basically that of the absence of a cause in the mechanistic scientific sense and is therefore unanalyzable by scientific thinking.

Our speculative conclusion is therefore that with regard to the problem of the existence of purpose in the creation, science, being uncommitted itself, offers no help. Like Maimonides[21] we may say that where reason fails we must choose to believe in creation by a purposeful creator for religious reasons. Like William James we may choose the will to believe for its pragmatic effects. Or with Bertrand Russell we may defiantly deny purposefulness to the creation. I do not propose to discuss the choice to be made. I wish only to show that in the light of contemporary science the choice still has to be made. The often assumed view that science permits no alternatives but requires the belief in the rigid rule of a purposeless mechanism through nature is no longer correct.

Of course it may always be asserted that scientific theory is notoriously unstable. Tomorrow's theory may discard today's use of creation and substitute some new mechanism. Plausible as such a view seems at first sight brief consideration shows it unsupported in fact by the history of science and irrelevant in theory to our conclusion that science is not committed to either a completely closed deterministic universe or to a purposeless creation.

The historical view shows us that much as science has progressed in giving a mechanistic account of the details of the world of experience it has never, except

---

21. Moses Maimonides, *Guide for the Perplexed*, Friedlander translation.

by unsupported extrapolation, even tackled the ultimate problems of the origin of matter or of man's conscious purposes. What seemed to nineteenth-century science as a necessary extrapolation of the mechanistic view to all problems including these ultimate questions is seen today to be not necessary at all. Whatever scientific theory may become dominant in the future is not important. What is important is that scientific theory has been unfrozen. It is not committed in advance to complete determinism. It can use both the concept of mechanism and also that of creation. Since it is uncommitted in theory, the fact that it is unstable simply emphasizes the irrelevance of any current point of view to the ultimate religious choices that the thinking mind must make.

Despite the fact, then, that man through science is ever pushing deeper into the details of the web of mechanism he is not being guided to any view of the pattern of the web as a whole. But perhaps this lack of intellectual commitment on the ultimate question of purpose that we find today in science is essential to man's freedom. For does not moral freedom depend upon an open intellect? If man were forced by the inescapable weight of scientific evidence to accept either the reality of purpose or of its absence in the universe would he be free to make a moral choice in his beliefs? Rationalistic philosophy in the centuries of its development has given no unequivocal answer to the problem of purpose in creation. Science likewise, despite the brashness shown in its youth, seems unable to offer help. Perhaps these failures are part of the moral structure of the universe, part of the human situation that is not to be changed as long as man is man. Man's intellectual and moral creativity require that he ever face the ultimate antinomy of chance versus purpose in the universe alone and unsupported by the crutch of either rational philosophy or objective science.[22]

---

22. The author wishes to take this occasion to express his indebtedness to Rabbi Akiba Predmesky for many stimulating discussions and explanations of rabbinic thought.

TRY THESE PROJECTS FOR—
SCIENCE AND CREATION,
by Etkin

1. *A simulated panel discussion or debate.*

   ▣ Scientist and religionist.

   ▣ Two kinds of scientists (religious and nonreligious) and two kinds of religionists (fundamentalist and naturalist or humanist).

   ▣ Two Orthodox scholars who disagree on whether the Torah can be reconciled with the theory of evolution.

   ▣ Any two who differ on the causes or purposes of creation and/or evolution.

   ▣ Three different kinds of evolutionists: materialist, vitalist, finalist (see discussion question No. 4 on page 49).

2. *Express yourself.*

   ▣ Draft a Reform Jewish "position statement" on science, religion, God, faith, creation, evolution, what have you. (Resource: The *CCAR Journal*, April, 1960.) If you like, have your resolution "worked over" by your instructor and fellow students, put it into final form, and send it to *Keeping Posted*, 838 Fifth Avenue, New York, N.Y. 10021.

   ▣ Book review of a recent work on science and religion. Follow this outline: Brief statement on main contents, author's main purpose, how well he succeeded, new ideas you gained, new questions raised in your mind.

   ▣ Responsa (replies to a query) as it might have been answered in different periods of history. Select a single query, such as, "Was the world created from nothing?" or "Had the world evolved?" or "Will the world ever end?" Address the query to a learned scribe in Bible days (Ezra?), to a medieval Jewish philosopher (Maimonides?), and to a modern Jewish thinker (Mordecai Kaplan?). How would each one answer? Send your imaginary query and responsa to *Keeping Posted*.

   ▣ Sermon, to be given to an adult congregation, on the text read aloud by the astronauts on the flight of Apollo 8 into space: "In the beginning God . . ." Arrange to deliver your sermon at an assembly or worship service, or to publish it in your school paper or congregational bulletin.

   ▣ Word power: The three essays and their questions so far have used a number of difficult but important words. Make sure you know their dictionary meaning, can use them when you speak and write (including spelling), and understand them when you hear them. Cull out words like *omnipotent* and *omnibeneficent*, *naturalism* and *superpersonal*, *cosmology* and *epistemology*. Make a poster, or distribute a glossary, or prepare and give a quiz.

■ Outline: You are beginning to see four kinds of persons who could be classified in two groups. Draw up an outline detailing the position of each person within his group:

Judaism and science are in conflict.
a. The nonreligious scientist (add subheads).
b. The fundamentalist Orthodox or Conservative Jew (add subheads).

Judaism and science are not in conflict.
a. The religious scientist (add subheads).
b. The liberal Orthodox, Conservative, or Reform Jew (add subheads).

If you have a different idea of your own on how the various positions should be outlined, go ahead and do it your way.

■ Suggestion box: Set up one in the room, and invite students to drop in suggestions about studying science and religion, ideas, and complaints they wish to give teachers, the rabbi, the principal, parents, the school board, younger pupils; public school science teachers, curriculum planners, school boards; textbook writers, magazine and newspaper editors, radio and tv program departments; etc. Collect, group, edit the suggestions, and get instructor's and class' approval for ones to be actually sent "to whom concerned." When you get replies, set up a bulletin board exhibit, connecting reply to suggestion with colored ribbons or some other device.

■ Class book: Start collecting your writings and those of other students, and begin arranging and editing them for an eventual class book or special issue of your school paper to be published at the end of the course.

■ Tell the group about some good new ideas, answers, and questions that came to your mind during:
a. A visit to a science museum or science show.
b. A science lecture, tv documentary, or news report.
c. A science-fiction movie or tv show.
d. A collection of science-fiction short stories or a science-fiction novel.

3. *Interview an Orthodox Jewish scientist.*

Prepare a list of questions to ask him.

■ Does he feel any conflict between his religious and his scientific life? Does one interfere in any way with the other?

■ As a scientist, what does he think of religion, faith, belief, revelation, God?

45

■ As an Orthodox Jew, what does he think about creation, evolution, chance, evil?

■ Does he feel a connection between his religious and his scientific life? Does one contribute in any way to the other?

4. *Research.*

■ Maimonides and the purpose of the universe and/or man. (Resource: *Guide for the Perplexed*, Chapter 3.)

■ Darwin's religious position. (Resources: *The Origin of the Species,* end of Chapter 15; The Descent of Man, Chapter 21.)

AFTER YOU HAVE READ—
SCIENCE AND CREATION,
by Etkin

Discuss these questions:

1. Etkin deals with two fundamental issues of both science and religion:
Creation of the world—Did it always exist as it is today (continuous creation, "steady-state")? Or did it originate at one point in time from a concentrated mass (explosion theory, "big-bang")? Or did God create it out of nothing? Creation of man—Did he evolve gradually? Or did he evolve after a sudden, unexplainable "leap" or "quantum-jump"? Or was he created outright just as he is today?

What difference does it make? If you say, "None," can you explain why scientists and religionists argue so hotly about it? If you say it does make a difference, can you point clearly and specifically to some aspect of your own personal life where it matters how or when or why the world and man came into existence?

2. Can a biologist who accepts evolution also accept the existence of God? Read, carefully and critically, the following statement by George W. Beadle, winner of a Nobel Prize in 1958 for his work in genetics. (Note and discuss how often he uses the terms "I believe," "I accept," "faith"; his attitude toward the biblical creation story; and his final comparison between the creation of a hydrogen atom and the creation of man.)

"Many people seem to feel that one cannot accept the findings of science and at the same time retain faith in the existence of God. As a scientist I disagree. I see no conflict between science and religion and in explanation will use an example from my own field, biology. I believe in organic evolution; that is, I believe that all organisms from the smallest submicroscopic viruses to man himself arose from simpler forms by processes that take place when and where conditions favor them.

"How did this happen? I accept the cosmologist's view that at one time the universe consisted solely of hydrogen, the simplest of all elements, and that from this one element the other elements and then molecules of ever-increasing complexity arose. Finally, out of inorganic material the first living molecules evolved and life was born on earth. I believe that this happened not by chance but in a natural and inevitable course of events; that life had to arise when conditions became favorable for it, just as certain reactions have to happen in a modern chemist's test tube when conditions are right. By equally inevitable stages complete living systems appeared, then creatures of greater complexity. Finally, man came into being—man with his unique ability to remember, reason, and communicate. This ability made cultural evolution possible as a supplement to biological evolution. With it religion, art, music, science, and technology came into the world. It is our ability to pass on to our children these and other elements of our cultural heritage that distinguish us from lower animals. I find this view of evolution exciting and awesome, but a nonscientist may think it is crassly materialistic, and thus in head-on collision with his faith that everything in the universe was created by the guiding higher intelligence we call God.

"But is there really a conflict? I believe not. The answer to the question of creation still remains in the realm of faith. In early biblical times, before science became an inseparable part of man's culture, it was believed as a matter of faith that man was created as man. Since then science has led us back through a sequence of evolutionary events in such a way that there is no logical place to stop—not with man, nor with the lower animals, nor with viruses—until we come to a primeval universe made of hydrogen. But then we ask, 'Whence came the hydrogen?' and science has no answer. Is it any less awe-inspiring to conceive of a universe created of hydrogen with the capacity to evolve into man than it is to accept the creation of man as man? I believe not. . . ."

3. Etkin finds a "gap" between man's evolution and that of apes, and says it is impossible to bridge this gap by the usual mechanisms of evolution. Here are two statements by another authority. Would Etkin accept them? Why or why not? Would you?

". . . the creative process of evolution is not to be interrupted by any supernatural intervention. The evolution of the first living cells from previously existing nonliving materials may represent a 'quantum-leap' rather than an infinitesimal step along the path of progress, but it is an entirely natural development. Biochemists are even now on the verge of discovering in great detail precisely how it could have taken place. In similar fashion, the emergence from ancestral anthropoid apes of human beings possessed of spiritual capacities enabling them to display an awareness of aesthetic values and ethical principles is no more miraculous than the emergence of the first air-breathing quadrupeds from their aquatic predecessors. The spiritual aspects of the life of men are just as surely a product of the processes called evolution as are his brain and nervous system." (Kirtley F. Mather, *Science Ponders Religion*, p. 38.)

"The inference is valid that man's awareness of aesthetic values and ethical principles is likewise a response to spiritual forces in the cosmic environment. There may well be a spiritual field, as well as a gravitational field and an electromagnetic field, to which adjustment may be made in accordance with the regulations of the evolutionary process." (*Ibid.*, p. 42.)

4. Rabbi Gunther Plaut, in *Judaism and the Scientific Spirit,* defines three major kinds of evolutionists. Which would Etkin agree with? Which do you agree with? In both cases, why?

Materialists say:

"Matter is not gifted with motives or purposes, and its evolution must be understood as a statistical phenomenon . . . Statistics has no 'purpose'; by definition it is accident or chance. . . . Man was not 'meant' to be created; he just happened, as 'the result of a purposeless and materialistic process that did have him in mind.'"

Vitalists say:

"Life produces and is propelled by a vital force, an inner surge and urge, an instinctual power and drive which Bergson called the *élan vital* . . . [which] finds its highest expression in the human mind. . . . The vitalist denies the supremacy of matter; and while his position is not necessarily a religious one, it does allow for belief in the divine origin of life and the divine nature of the soul."

Finalists say:

"Evolution has a grand design built into it from its humble, one-cellular beginnings. It drives towards purposed goals. While the strict materialist holds that evolution has no goals, the finalist asserts the opposite. To him, the appearance of man on nature's scene is not the result of chance. Who then provided the master plan? Some finalists will say 'Nature'; others will say 'God.'"

5. Two Orthodox Jewish scholars state their views on whether or not Torah and evolution are reconcilable:

"The Torah specifies each creature *after its kind*—to teach that the species are *fixed;* there is no transition from one to another, as the theory of evolution posits for all nature . . . Especially as regards the creation of man, the verses of the Bible (Genesis 1:26; 2:7) . . . literally contradict the theory of evolution." (Menahem M. Kasher.)

". . . there is nothing inherently un-Jewish in the evolutionary conception of the origin and growth of forms of existence from the simple to the complex, and from the lowest to the highest. The biblical account itself gives expression to the same general truth of gradual ascent from amorphous chaos to order, from inorganic to organic, from lifeless matter to vegetable, animal, and man. . . (Rabbi J. H. Hertz.)

Read Genesis, Chapter 1, carefully and thoughtfully and decide for yourself who is right. If you agree with Rabbi Hertz, what do you think is the *real* difference between Genesis, Chapter 1, and the theory of evolution? (You'll find Rabbi Hertz's answer on page 194 of his commentary on The Pentateuch and the Haftorahs.)

6. How far can we go with the scientific evidence on the creation of the universe, and what happens after we reach the limits of that evidence? As one writer puts it:

"... the trouble with cosmology is that it is incomplete, it's philosophically unsatisfying, and it always leads to ultimate questions which are outside science." (C. P. Gilmore, "The Birth and Life of the Universe," *The New York Times Magazine,* June 12, 1966.)

What are some of these "ultimate" questions outside the realm of science? What are your personal answers to them?

7. Consider this "picture" drawn by a Reform rabbi. Would Etkin accept it? If it is a correct picture, what religious beliefs follow from it?

"Our Earth is a junior member of our Sun's planetary system."

"Our Sun is one of the smaller stars in our Milky Way Galaxy."

"Our Milky Way Galaxy is composed of about a million sun-like stars, each with its own planetary system."

"Our Milky Way Galaxy is only one of about 100 million such galaxies observable in the Universe."

"Our Universe has no beginning in time. It seems to be an eternal process of continuous creation."

"Somewhere in the vast background of space a tenuous gas exists out of which the components of galaxies are condensed. This raw-material gas just is, always was, and always will be."

"The galaxies do have an origin in time. The oldest go back about 10 billion years."

"Our Milky Way Galaxy is no more than 5 billion years old. A billion years of clouding and condensation within the clouds resulted in the formation of the oldest stars in our galaxy."

"One of them is our Sun. It was a binary—a kind of twin—some other star kept whirling about it until two-and-a-half billion years ago when an explosion occurred. The fragments of our Sun's twin brother were blown into distant space. One wisp of gas escaped the long ride. It somehow clung to the Sun's area and proceeded to cloud and condense into our planetary system in which our Earth is a junior member."

"Our Earth, therefore, is two-and-a-half billion years old."

"The first trace of life in our Earth dates back 1,7000,000,000 years. This primeval cell split and split and its offspring specialized until it developed into a kind of fish. The fish gave birth to a family of mammals about 60 million years ago."

"The mammals branched off into anthropoid apes some 8 million years ago."

"And in 1929, we discovered the remains of the earliest man at Chan Kan Tien, China, who came on the scene about one million years ago." (Ely Pilchik, *From the Beginning.*)

8. In the "Before You Read" section you labeled eight statements true or false. According to this article, Etkin would have labeled them all the same way—all true, or all false. Reread the article, or skim over it, to find a few places where the statements come up and see what the pattern is. Then take any statements you mislabeled, and search the article carefully to see where and how Etkin deals with it.

A
FREE
MAN'S
WORSHIP,
by Russell

Choose which ending below you agree with most.

If you don't like any of them, try to write an ending of your own.

1. Life is   (a) sad   (b) happy   (c) sad, but we can make it happier   (d)

2. Atheism, compared to theism, requires   (a) no faith   (b) less faith   (c) more faith   (d)

3. An atheist philosophy of life, compared to a theist philosophy, makes   (a) no sense   (b) as much sense   (c) more sense   (d)

4. Compared to a theist, an atheist trying to justify ethical principles finds it   (a) impossible   (b) easier   (c) just as hard   (d)

5. God   (a) exists, is all-powerful, and good   (b) exists, is all-powerful, and evil   (c) does not exist, and man has imagined or created Him   (d)

6. For man, the universe is (a) bad and dangerous   (b) good and wholesome   (c) bad and dangerous, but we can make it better and safer   (d)

7. God   (a) wants to prevent evil but cannot do it   (b) could prevent evil but doesn't want to   (c) uses evil to punish those who violate His laws   (d)

8. Our universe is   (a) hostile and has no purpose   (b) hostile but has a purpose   (c) friendly and has a purpose   (d)

9. People observe the rules of morality because   (a) the police power of the state will punish them if they don't   (b) it's prudent for them if they do ("honesty is the best policy")   (c) it's the best way for all of us to get along together in an otherwise meaningless world   (d)

10. Things happen in our universe   (a) because they are part of an overall plan in the "mind" of God   (b) because of natural laws   (c) because of our own actions and reactions   (d)

A FREE MAN'S WORSHIP

Bertrand Russell

In this essay, which has now become a classic, one of the most distinguished philosophers of our time evaluates the place of man in a materialistic universe.

To Dr. Faustus in his study Mephistopheles told the history of the creation, saying:

"The endless praises of the choirs of angels had begun to grow wearisome; for, after all, did he not deserve their praise? Had he not given them endless joy? Would it not be more amusing to obtain undeserved praise, to be worshipped by beings whom he tortured? He smiled inwardly, and resolved that the great drama should be performed.

"For countless ages the hot nebula whirled aimlessly through space. At length it began to take shape, the central mass threw off planets, the planets cooled, boiling seas and burning mountains heaved and tossed, from black masses of cloud hot sheets of rain deluged the barely solid crust. And now the first germ of life grew in the depths of the ocean, and developed rapidly in the fructifying warmth into vast forest trees, huge ferns springing from the damp mould, sea monsters breeding, fighting, devouring, and passing away. And from the monsters, as the play unfolded itself, Man was born, with the power of thought, the knowledge of good and evil, and the cruel thirst for worship. And Man saw that all is passing in this mad, monstrous world, that all is struggling to snatch, at any cost, a few brief moments of life before Death's inexorable decree. And Man said: 'There is a hidden purpose, could we but fathom it, and the purpose is good; for we must reverence something, and in the visible world there is nothing worthy of reverence.' And Man stood aside from the struggle, resolving that God intended harmony to come out of chaos by human efforts. And when he followed the instincts of which God had transmitted to him from his ancestry of beasts of prey, he called it Sin, and asked God to forgive him. But he doubted whether he could be justly forgiven, until he invented a divine plan by which God's wrath was to have been appeased. And seeing the present was bad, he made it yet worse, that thereby the future might be better. And he gave God thanks for the strength that enabled him to forgo even the joys that were possible. And God smiled; and when he saw that Man had become perfect in renunciation and worship, he sent another sun through the sky, which crashed into Man's sun; and all returned again to nebula.

"'Yes,' he murmured, 'it was a good play; I will have it performed again.'"

Such, in outline, but even more purposeless, more void of meaning, is the world which Science presents for our belief. Amid such a world, if anywhere, our ideals henceforward must find a home. That Man is the product of causes which had no prevision of the end they were achieving; that his origin, his growth, his hopes and fears, his loves and his beliefs, are but the outcome of accidental collocations of atoms; that no fire, no heroism, no intensity of thought and feeling, can preserve an individual life beyond the grave; that all the labours of the ages, all the devotion, all the inspiration, all the noonday brightness of human genius, are destined to extinction in the vast death of the solar system, and that the whole temple of Man's achievement must inevitably be buried beneath the débris of a universe in ruins—all these things, if not quite beyond dispute, are yet so nearly certain, that no philosophy which rejects them can hope to stand. Only within the scaffolding of these truths, only on the firm foundation of unyielding despair, can the soul's habitation henceforth be safely built.

How, in such an alien and inhuman world, can so powerless a creature as Man preserve his aspirations untarnished? A strange mystery it is that Nature, omnipotent but blind, in the revolutions of her secular hurryings through the abysses of space, has brought forth at last a child, subject still to her power, but gifted with sight, with knowledge of good and evil, with the capacity of judging all the works of his unthinking Mother. In spite of Death, the mark and seal of the parental control, Man is yet free, during his brief years, to examine, to criticise, to know, and in imagination to create. To him alone, in the world with which he is acquainted, this freedom belongs; and in this lies his superiority to the resistless forces that control his outward life.

The savage, like ourselves, feels the oppression of his impotence before the powers of Nature; but having in himself nothing that he respects more than Power, he is willing to prostrate himself before his gods, without inquiring whether they are worthy of his worship. Pathetic and very terrible is the long history of cruelty and torture, of degradation and human sacrifice, endured in the hope of placating the jealous gods: surely, the trembling believer thinks, when what is most precious has been freely given, their lust for blood must be appeased, and more will not be required. The religion of Moloch—as such creeds may be generically called—is in essence the cringing submission of the slave, who dare not, even in his heart, allow the thought that his master deserves no adulation. Since the independence of ideals is not yet acknowledged, Power may be freely worshipped, and receive an unlimited respect, despite its wanton infliction of pain.

But gradually, as morality grows bolder, the claim of the ideal world begins to be felt; and worship, if it is not to cease, must be given to gods of another kind than those created by the savage. Some, though they feel the demands of the ideal, will still consciously reject them, still urging that naked Power is worthy of worship. Such is the attitude inculcated in God's answer to Job out of the whirlwind: the divine power and knowledge are paraded, but of the divine goodness there is no hint. Such also is the attitude of those who, in our own day, base their morality upon the struggle for survival, maintaining that the survivors are necessarily the fittest. But others, not content with an answer so repugnant to the moral sense, will adopt the position which we have become accustomed to regard as specially religious, maintaining that, in some hidden manner, the world of fact is really harmonious with the world of ideals. Thus Man creates God, all-powerful and all-good, the mystic unity of what is and what should be.

But the world of fact, after all, is not good; and, in submitting our judgment to it, there is an element of slavishness from which our thoughts must be purged.

For in all things it is well to exalt the dignity of Man, by freeing him as far as possible from the tyranny of nonhuman Power. When we have realized that Power is largely bad, that man, with his knowledge of good and evil, is but a helpless atom in a world which has no such knowledge, the choice is again presented to us: Shall we worship Force, or shall we worship Goodness? Shall our God exist and be evil, or shall he be recognized as the creation of our own conscience?

The answer to this question is very momentous, and affects profoundly our whole morality. The worship of Force, to which Carlyle and Nietzsche and the creed of Militarism have accustomed us, is the result of failure to maintain our own ideals against a hostile universe: it is itself a prostrate submission to evil, a sacrifice of our best to Moloch. If strength indeed is to be respected, let us respect rather the strength of those who refuse that false "recognition of facts" which fails to recognize that facts are often bad. Let us admit that, in the world we know, there are many things that would be better otherwise, and that the ideals to which we do and must adhere are not realized in the realm of matter. Let us preserve our respect for truth, for beauty, for the ideal of perfection which life does not permit us to attain, though none of these things meet with the approval of the unconscious universe. If Power is bad, as it seems to be, let us reject it from our hearts. In this lies Man's true freedom: in determination to worship only the God created by our own love of the good, to respect only the heaven which inspires the insight of our best moments. In action, in desire, we must submit perpetually to the tyranny of outside forces; but in thought, in aspiration, we are free, free from our fellow men, free from the petty planet on which our bodies impotently crawl, free even, while we live, from the tyranny of Death. Let us learn, then, that energy of faith which enables us to live constantly in the vision of the good; and let us descend, in action, into the world of fact, with that vision always before us.

When first the opposition of fact and ideal grows fully visible, a spirit of fiery revolt, of fierce hatred of the gods, seems necessary to the assertion of freedom. To defy with Promethean constancy a hostile universe, to keep its evil always in view, always actively hated, to refuse no pain that the malice of Power can invent, appears to be the duty of all who will not bow before the inevitable. But indignation is still a bondage, for it compels our thoughts to be occupied with an evil world; and in the fierceness of desire from which rebellion springs there is a kind of self-assertion which it is necessary for the wise to overcome. Indignation is a submission of our thoughts, but not of our desires; the Stoic freedom in which wisdom consists is found in the submission of our desires, but not of our thoughts. From the submission of our desires springs the virtue of resignation; from the freedom of our thoughts springs the whole world of art and philosophy, and the vision of beauty by which, at last, we half reconquer the reluctant world. But the vision of beauty is possible only to unfettered contemplation, to thoughts not weighted by the load of eager wishes; and thus Freedom comes only to those who no longer ask of life that it shall yield them any of those personal goods that are subject to the mutations of Time.

Although the necessity of renunciation is evidence of the existence of evil, yet Christianity, in preaching it, has shown a wisdom exceeding that of the Promethean philosophy of rebellion. It must be admitted that, of the things we desire, some, though they prove impossible, are yet real goods; others, however, as ardently longed for, do not form part of a fully purified ideal. The belief that what must be renounced is bad, though sometimes false, is far less often false than untamed passion supposes; and the creed of religion, by providing a reason for proving that it is never false, has been the means of purifying our hopes by the discovery of many austere truths.

But there is in resignation a further good element: even real goods, when they are unattainable, ought not to be fretfully desired. To every man comes, sooner or later, the great renunciation. For the young, there is nothing unattainable; a good thing desired with the whole force of a passionate will, and yet impossible, is to them not credible. Yet, by death, by illness, by poverty, or by the voice of duty, we must learn, each one of us, that the world was not made for us, and that, however beautiful may be the things we crave, Fate may nevertheless forbid them. It is the part of courage, when misfortune comes, to bear without repining the ruin of our hopes, to turn away our thoughts from vain regrets. This degree of submission to Power is not only just and right: it is the very gate of wisdom.

But passive renunciation is not the whole of wisdom; for not by renunciation alone can we build a temple for the worship of our own ideals. Haunting foreshadowings of the temple appear in the realm of imagination, in music, in architecture, in the untroubled kingdom of reason, and in the golden sunset magic of lyrics, where beauty shines and glows, remote from the touch of sorrow, remote from the fear of change, remote from the failures and disenchantments of the world of fact. In the contemplation of these things the vision of heaven will shape itself in our hearts, giving at once a touchstone to judge the world about us and an inspiration by which to fashion to our needs whatever is not incapable of serving as a stone in the sacred temple.

Except for those rare spirits that are born without sin, there is a cavern of darkness to be traversed before that temple can be entered. The gate of the cavern is despair, and its floor is paved with the gravestones of abandoned hopes. There Self must die; there the eagerness, the greed of untamed desire must be slain, for only so can the soul be freed from the empire of Fate. But out of the cavern the Gate of Renunciation leads again to the daylight of wisdom, by whose radiance a new insight, a new joy, a new tenderness, shine forth to gladden the pilgrim's heart.

When, without the bitterness of impotent rebellion, we have learnt both to resign ourselves to the outward rule of Fate and to recognize that the nonhuman world is unworthy of our worship, it becomes possible at last so to transform and refashion the unconscious universe, so to transmute it in the crucible of imagination, that a new image of shining gold replaces the old idol of clay. In all the multiform facts of the world—in the visual shapes of trees and mountains and clouds, in the events of the life of Man, even in the very omnipotence of Death—the insight of creative idealism can find the reflection of a beauty which its own thoughts first made. In this way mind asserts its subtle mastery over the thoughtless forces of Nature. The more evil the material with which it deals, the more thwarting to untrained desire, the greater is its achievement in inducing the reluctant rock to yield up its hidden treasures, the prouder its victory in compelling the opposing forces to swell the pageant of its triumph. Of all the arts, Tragedy is the proudest, the most triumphant; for it builds its shining citadel in the very centre of the enemy's country, on the very summit of his highest mountain; from its impregnable watchtowers, his camps and arsenals, his columns and forts, are all revealed; within its walls the free life continues, while the legions of Death and Pain and Despair, and all the servile captains of tyrant Fate, afford the burghers of that dauntless city new spectacles of beauty. Happy those sacred ramparts, thrice happy the dwellers on that all-seeing eminence. Honour to those brave warriors who, through countless ages of warfare, have preserved for us the priceless heritage of liberty, and have kept undefiled by sacrilegious invaders the home of the unsubdued.

But the beauty of Tragedy does but make visible a quality which, in more or less obvious shapes, is present always and everywhere in life. In the spectacle of Death, in the endurance of intolerable pain, and in the irrevocableness of a vanished past, there is a sacredness, an overpowering awe, a feeling of the vastness, the depth, the inexhaustible mystery of existence, in which, as by some strange marriage of pain, the sufferer is bound to the world by bonds of sorrow. In these moments of insight, we lose all eagerness of temporary desire, all struggling and striving for petty ends, all care for the little trivial things that, to a superficial view, make up the common life of day by day; we see, surrounding the narrow raft illumined by the flickering light of human comradeship, the dark ocean on whose rolling waves we toss for a brief hour; from the great night without, a chill blast breaks in upon our refuge; all the loneliness of humanity amid hostile forces is concentrated upon the individual soul, which must struggle alone, with what of courage it can command, against the whole weight of a universe that cares nothing for its hopes and fears. Victory, in this struggle with the powers of darkness, is the true baptism into the glorious company of heroes, the true initiation into the overmastering beauty of human existence. From that awful encounter of the soul with the outer world, enunciation, wisdom, and charity are born; and with their birth a new life begins. To take into the inmost shrine of the soul the irresistible forces whose puppets we seem to be—Death and change, the irrevocableness of the Past, and the powerlessness of Man before the blind hurry of the universe from vanity to vanity—to feel these things and know them is to conquer them.

This is the reason why the Past has such magical power. The beauty of its motionless and silent pictures is like the enchanted purity of late autumn, when the leaves, though one breath would make them fall, still glow against the sky in golden glory. The Past does not change or strive; like Duncan, after life's fitful fever it sleeps well; what was eager and grasping, what was petty and transitory, has faded away, the things that were beautiful and eternal shine out of it like stars in the night. Its beauty, to a soul not worthy of it, is unendurable; but to a soul which has conquered Fate it is the key of religion.

The life of Man, viewed outwardly, is but a small thing in comparison with the forces of Nature. The slave is doomed to worship Time and Fate and Death, because they are greater than anything he finds in himself, and because all his thoughts are of things which they devour. But, great as they are, to think of them greatly, to feel their passionless splendour, is greater still. And such thought makes us free men; we no longer bow before the inevitable in Oriental subjection, but we absorb it, and make it a part of ourselves. To abandon the struggle for private happiness, to expel all eagerness of temporary desire, to burn with passion for eternal things—this is emancipation, and this is the free man's worship. And this liberation is effected by the mind which leaves nothing to be purged by the purifying fire of Time.

United with his fellow men by the strongest of all ties, the tie of a common doom, the free man finds that a new vision is with him always, shedding over every daily task the light of love. The life of Man is a long march through the night, surrounded by invisible foes, tortured by weariness and pain, towards a goal that few can hope to reach, and where none may tarry long. One by one, as they march, our comrades vanish from our sight, seized by the silent orders of omnipotent Death. Very brief is the time in which we can help them, in which their happiness or misery is decided. Be it ours to shed sunshine on their path, to lighten their sorrows by the balm of sympathy, to give them the pure joy of a never-tiring affection, to strengthen failing courage, to instil faith in hours of despair. Let us not weigh in grudging scales their merits and demerits, but let us think only of their need—of the sorrows, the difficulties, perhaps the blindnesses, that make the misery of their lives; let us remember that they are fellow sufferers in the same darkness, actors in the same tragedy with ourselves. And so, when their day is over, when their good and their evil have become eternal by the immortality of the Past, be it ours to feel that, where they suffered, where they failed, no deed of ours was the cause; but wherever a spark of the divine fire kindled in their hearts, we were ready with encouragement, with sympathy, with brave words in which high courage glowed.

Brief and powerless is Man's life; on him and all his race the slow, sure doom falls pitiless and dark. Blind to good and evil, reckless of destruction, omnipotent matter rolls on its relentless way; for Man, condemned today to lose his dearest, tomorrow himself to pass through the gate of darkness, it remains only to cherish, ere yet the blow falls, the lofty thoughts that ennoble his little day; disdaining the coward terrors of the slave of Fate, to worship at the shrine that his own hands have built; undismayed by the empire of chance, to preserve a mind free from the wanton tyranny that rules his outward life; proudly defiant of the irresistible forces that tolerate, for a moment, his knowledge and his condemnation, to sustain alone, a weary but unyielding Atlas, the world that his own ideals have fashioned despite the trampling march of unconscious Power.

TRY THESE PROJECTS FOR—
A FREE MAN'S WORSHIP,
by Russell

1. *Express yourself.*

■ Write a synopsis or summary of Russell's essay, in which, using your own words, you condense his ideas into a paragraph of five to ten sentences. If you enjoy this kind of challenge, and want to be especially helpful to fellow students, do the same for other essays in this unit. Your work can appear in a special issue of the school paper or in a final class book, or you can give it out to students for reviews.

■ As you attend services, listen to the rabbi's sermons especially for content related to problems of this unit—science, religion, proof, knowledge, faith, belief, creation, evolution, nature of our universe, etc. Whenever you hear something relevant to this unit, ask your rabbi if you may examine a copy of that sermon. Copy out significant passages, and then in your own words draw up a statement of the rabbi's position. Let him see and correct it before you present it to your instructor or the class. If your statement raises questions in anyone's mind, invite the rabbi to visit the class and clarify them.

■ Using Russell's words and/or your own, compose a prayer that he would accept as fitting "a free man's worship." Make clear to whom or what he prays, what for, and why. Since prayer includes more than just "asking" for something, consider whether or not Russell would offer praise (of what?), give thanks (to whom, for what?), confess wrongdoing, make promises or pledges, and so on. Read or distribute "Russell's Prayer" to the class, and ask their opinion on whether it would be acceptable to them as part of Jewish worship.

2. *Plan—and if possible, actually produce—a radio or tv program, a film, filmstrip, or slide set.*

■ Act out scenes from Macleish's *J. B.*, the biblical story of Job, and/or the version in *There Was a Man . . .* by Maxwell Silver.

■ Try a sociodrama in which Job confronts Abraham and wants to know why God answered Abraham's doubts one way and his own another.

■ A round table in which Townes, Einstein, Etkin, and Russell answer a few specific questions selected from those in this unit, your own questions, or both.

■ "This Is Your Life" program. This was a popular radio and tv show in which a celebrity was unexpectedly confronted with people, photos, films, and voices from his past. Make *your* celebrity man, and show him *his* past in the same way—using real or imaginary material, actual or simulated sounds and sights, or anything at all that enables you to say to all mankind, "This Is Your Life." Your very first problem: What point of view will you take? Russell's? Townes'? Einstein's? Etkin's? Or Bemporad's (see next essay)? Or will you try a "double" "This Is Your Life"—showing both points of view, side by side, or one after the other? Be sure to check out the statements by Pilchik, discussion question No. 7 for Etkin's "Science and Creation," on pages 50-51.

■ A "single-concept" film on a concept in this unit, or of two concepts that support or contradict each other. If you have the equipment, a little know-how, and lots of creative imagination, such a film is great fun and not too much work. For general and technical guidance write to Eastman Kodak Company, 343 State Street, Rochester, N.Y. 14650, for a copy of their free booklet, *Movies with a Purpose*. Use original sketches, cartoons, and diagrams, available photos and filmstrip frames or slides, animation, taped voices, musical backgrounds, what have you. Sample scenario: Worship as Russell sees it (primitive man, slave, Promethean, Stoic, the free man), with vocal comment, agreement, disagreement by fellow students, your rabbi, a scientist, mathematician, or philosopher in your congregation, etc.

3. *Answer back!*

■ Design and sketch a series of cartoons for Russell's article. If you generally oppose his way of thinking, then your cartoons will poke fun at him. For example: Show Russell writing, "The life of Man, viewed outwardly, is but a small thing in comparison with the forces of nature," and surround him with sketches of animal species completely wiped out by man, and the whole world being blown up by a man-created nuclear explosion. If, on the other hand, you generally accept Russell's philosophy, then your cartoons will poke fun at his opponents. For example: A prayer describing God as all-powerful, all-knowing, all-good, surrounded by sketches of horrible disasters, the Nazi holocaust, innocent young babies dying in accidents or from diseases, acts of crime, etc. Our responsibilities to our fellow men, according to Russell, are entirely emotional and intellectual. We must "shed sunshine on their path . . . lighten their sorrows by . . . sympathy . . . give them . . . a never-tiring affection . . . strengthen failing courage . . . instil faith in hours of despair . . . think only of their need . . . of the sorrows, difficulties, perhaps the blindnesses, that make the misery of their lives . . . remember that they are fellow sufferers in the same darkness, actors in the same tragedy with ourselves. . . ." Find a way you can carry out an equally vital responsibility toward others that he ignores—*action to prevent or correct failure, sorrows, difficulties, blindnesses, misery, darkness, and tragedy.* For example: Find something wrong going on that you personally or with students can help to end or change; then do it. Make it something local, immediate, and small enough for you to be personally involved and to see some improvement in a reasonable time. Experience the feeling of "overcoming" in contrast to Russell's "helplessness"; and then try to carry this feeling over to larger, more complicated, more time-consuming action against evil.

4. *Find examples from your own personal experience of times when you felt, spoke, or acted in accordance with each of the following "philosophies."*

■Prometheanism: Raging revolt against an injustice.

■Stoicism: Accepting an unpleasant task without hope of reward simply because it has to be done; learning to control emotions, overcome fear, accept failure and disappointment calmly and hopefully.

■Desperation: The whole world is hopelessly against you, and your only recourse is to bury yourself in your own dreams and thoughts.

■Hope: No matter how bad things look now you see a chance for improvement and are eager to get started.

■Religion: A sense of support and help coming to you in your effort to find out what is right and what is wrong and how to increase one and decrease the other.

■Judaism: A feeling of inspiration, obligation, and happiness in tackling life in a Jewish way.

Write these experiences up in the form of an imaginary diary—you may fictionalize, exaggerate, be humorous, if you like. The point: To show how the same person at different times, under different conditions, reacts in different ways. If you prefer, write up such an imaginary diary for Russell, to show how even a philosopher acts and reacts in various ways, no matter how he insists we ought to act and react.

5. *Research projects.*

■The concept of God and the Nazi holocaust. (Resources: Hans Jonas, "The Concept of God after Auschwitz," in *Out of the Whirlwind;* Richard Rubenstein, *After Auschwitz, What?;* Jack Bemporad, "Toward a New Jewish Theology," in *American Judaism,* Winter, 1964–1965.)

■Do scientists believe in God? (Resource: Warren Weaver, "Can a Scientist Believe in God?" in *A Guide to the Religions of America.*)

■Different viewpoints on the story of Job. (Resources: The Book of Job in the Bible; Archibald Macleish, *J. B.;* Dr. Joseph Mindel, "Sparks Fly Upward," *Eternal Light* script; Maxwell Silver, *There Was a Man . . .*)

■ The legend of Faust—Its relationship to Russell's view of the universe, and that of Judaism.

■ Stoicism—Its founder, Zeno, and his philosophy, compared with Russell and with Judaism. (Resources: Encyclopedias.)

After You Have Read—
A FREE MAN'S WORSHIP,
by Russell

Discuss these questions:

1. Russell gives us two choices: "Shall we worship Force, or shall we worship Goodness? Shall our God exist and be evil, or shall he be recognized as the creation of our own conscience?" Is there a third choice that he omits? Suppose God exists, and hates evil, but can't prevent it? If He can't, why not? Why do you suppose Russell overlooked this third choice—didn't even bring it up and try to rebut it?

2. Study the following passages. Are the writers affirming a God who is not all-powerful? What reasons do they give to support their conclusions? Compare their concepts of creativity, freedom, and choice with Russell's.

"On a purely logical basis the concept of God's omnipotence is self-contradictory. Absolute, total power means power not limited by anything, not even by the mere existence of something other than the possessor of that power; for the very existence of such another would already constitute a limitation, and the one would have to annihilate it so as to save its absoluteness. Absolute power then in its solitude has no object on which to act. But as objectless power it is a powerless power, cancelling itself out: 'All' equals 'zero' here. In order for it to act there must be something else, and as soon as there is, the one is not all-powerful anymore, even though in any comparison its power may be superior by any degree you please to imagine. The existence of another object limits the power of the most powerful agent at the same time that it allows it to be an agent. In brief, power as such is a relational concept and requires relation." (Hans Jonas, "The Concept of God after Auschwitz" in *Out of the Whirlwind*.)

"If God is defined as omnipotent and omniscient in the traditional sense, then man's freedom is limited to a reenacting of a pattern already in God's mind. This means that man does not genuinely create or decide anything. Creativity and freedom means the capacity to decide what is really undecided. They imply an open future with real alternative possibilities; the real determination of what is essentially indeterminate. Judaism affirms that man has a real choice and is responsible for that choice; it affirms that his choice makes a difference for good or for evil to man himself and to the universe in which man lives. Therefore, a new theology, in order to vindicate the power and creativity of man, must endeavor to show that omnipotence cannot mean all possible power. In short, it must be recognized that there are limitations to God's power other than purely logical ones." (Jack Bemporad, "Toward a New Jewish Theology" in *American Judaism*, Winter 1964–65.)

3. Study the following passage and then answer the questions below.

"To regard God as perfect in power, as He is in vision, at the very beginning is the most disastrous of superstitions . . . and the most momentous decision which mankind has to make is to learn on that score. God and man are a polarity. They are both heroes in the same drama. They need each other, they grow together, but they also suffer together." (Henry Slonimsky, *Essays*.)

How can God be perfect in vision but not in power?

According to this statement, God "needs," "grows," and "suffers." It's easy to understand these terms for *man*—but what exactly do they mean for God? Are these terms examples of anthropomorphism—talking of God as if He were a human being? Or do they correctly represent a relationship between God and man something like the relationship between a parent and a child?

According to "The Guiding Principles of Reform Judaism," issued in 1937 by the Central Conference of American Rabbis, "Man is God's copartner." What familiar prayers in Jewish worship come to mind that express this idea? That express the opposite idea (or "superstition" as Slonimsky calls it) that God is the supreme Master and Ruler of everyone and everything? Which of the two ideas is closer to your own personal feeling about God?

4. Suppose God is not all-powerful and therefore cannot prevent all possible evil and suffering—or that He can, but for good reasons of His own chooses not to—but He has created a world where men can prevent a great deal of evil and suffering if they want to and learn how to. What conclusion follows about whether the world is finished or unfinished? If it's unfinished, who's supposed to finish it—God? Man? God and man? If God and man, what is the role of each? Could the prophet Zechariah have had such ideas in mind in saying, "On that day the Lord shall be One and His name One"? (Zechariah 14:9.) When and how do we recite this verse in Jewish worship so as to give it a very special emphasis?

5. When is it right to defy, resist, and rebel against evil (the "Promethean" reaction), and when is it right to be passive, resigned, and accepting (the "Stoic" reaction)? Is there a general principle to follow? What is the answer of Judaism? Give specific examples from Jewish history to prove your point.

6. Glance over the three essays in this course by Ferry, Weinberg, and Hertz, then react to the following passage from Russell. Is man actually as powerless as Russell claims?

"Death and change, the irrevocableness of the Past, and the powerlessness of Man before the blind hurry of the universe from vanity to vanity—to feel these things and know them is to conquer them."

66

7. According to Freud, life is "a little island of pain in a vast sea of indifference." Would Russell agree? Would Townes, Einstein, or Etkin? Does Judaism agree? (Give specific evidence.) Do you agree?

8. In the following passage from Russell, substitute the word "hope" for "despair." Does the sentence then make just as good sense? More sense? If either one, how do you react to a sentence where you can reverse the key word and still get as much sense or more?

". . . only on the firm foundation of unyielding despair can the soul's habitation henceforth be safely built."

In the same way, try substituting "glorious future" for "doom" in Russell's following statement:

"United with his fellow men by the strongest of all ties, the tie of a common doom, the free man finds that a new vision is with him always, shedding over every daily task the light of love."

How do people actually build their soul's habitation or find a new vision shedding the light of love—out of despair or out of hope?

9. Russell apparently sees man and the universe as different, opposed, alien to each other—one is bad, the other desires the good, and "never the twain shall meet." Consider the opposite theory—that man is an organic part of the universe, which keeps him alive as well as kills him, heals as well as hurts him, encourages his highest ideals as well as his most brutal impulses. If our good dreams, hopes, ideals are also part of the universe, it must therefore contain "good" as well as "bad." Before you answer the next question, look over Genesis, Chapter 1, the *Shehecheyanu* blessing we recite every holiday, and the *Birkat ha-Mazon* (Grace) we recite after meals.

Does Judaism see the universe as for you? Against you? Neither? Both? How do you see the universe?

10. Look back at your answers to the "Before You Read" section for this essay. For how many of them did you accept one of the given answers (a, b, or c)? For how many did you add a better answer of your own (d)? The "a-b-c" choices in each case were all based on Russell's viewpoint—and in each case they left out another possible choice (d) that he ignored. Here are the "d" answers that would have given you a fairer choice. How many of them do you accept? What other answers did you think of yourself?

   1. Life is both sad and happy; we can make it happier than it is, and we can learn to deal with the sadness.
   2. Atheism, compared to theism, requires as much faith.
   3. An atheist philosophy, compared to a theist one, makes less sense.

4. Compared to a theist, an atheist trying to justify ethical principles finds it harder.
5. God exists and is more powerful than anything we know, but not all-powerful.
6. For man, the universe is both dangerous and wholesome; we can make it still safer and healthier and can learn to survive the danger.
7. God wants to prevent evil, but actually does it only through human effort.
8. Our universe is both hostile and friendly, and has order and purpose.
9. People observe morality because they believe the world can be a better place to live in and it's their job to try and make it so.
10. Things happen in our universe sometimes by chance, sometimes according to natural laws, and sometimes because of our own actions and reactions—and all these are part of God's plan.

THE DUNCE

And 'Science' said,
'Attention, Child, to me!
Have I not taught you all
You touch; taste; hear; and see?

'Nought that's true knowledge now
In print is pent
Which my sole method
Did not circumvent.

'Think you, the amoeba
In its primal slime
Wasted on dreams
Its destiny sublime?

'Yet, when I bid
Your eyes survey the board
Whereon life's How, When, Where
I now record,

'I find them fixed
In daydream; and you sigh;
Or, like a silly sheep,
You bleat me, Why?

' "Why is the grass so cool, and fresh, and green?
The sky so deep, and blue?"
Get to your Chemistry,
You dullard, you!

' "Why must I sit at books, and learn, and learn,
Yet long to play?"
Where's your Psychology,
You popinjay?

' "Why stay I here,
Not where my heart would be?"
Wait, dunce, and ask that
Of Philosophy!

'Reason is yours
Wherewith to con your task;
Not that unanswerable
Questions you should ask.

'Stretch out your hands, then—
Grubby, shallow bowl—
And be refreshed, Child—
Mind, and, maybe soul!

'Then—when you grow into
A man—like me;
You will as learnèd, wise,
And—happy be!'

Walter de la Mare

BEFORE YOU READ—

Ask yourself:

Could each of the following statements be accepted by a modern rabbi? Put YES or NO accordingly in the left-hand column. Could each statement be accepted by a modern scientist? Put YES or NO in the right-hand column. If not sure, put a question mark. Remember—the YES or NO does not mean you, but a modern rabbi or a modern scientist.

A Modern
Rabbi
                A Modern
Scientist

_____ 1.The universe has meaning, order, purpose. _____

_____ 2.The universe is the result of chance and contains no inherent values. _____

_____ 3.Man is an animal. _____

_____ 4.Man is not an animal. _____

_____ 5.Values are part of the entire universe. _____

_____ 6.Values are part of human life only. _____

_____ 7.There is a force or intelligence responsible for the way things are. _____

_____ 8.The idea of God is absolutely necessary. _____

_____ 9.There is evidence of a designing and controlling power in the universe. _____

_____ 10.Man needs both science and religion. _____

_____ 11.Whatever we have today has evolved by chance. _____

_____ 12.Science deals with what is, religion with what ought to be. _____

_____ 13. Science, dealing with a closed world, must "prove" its truths; religion, dealing with an unfinished world, must "actualize" its truths.   _____

_____ 14. Creation took place exactly as described in Genesis.   _____

_____ 15. All men are descended from one source of life.   _____

_____ 16. God is responsible for everything in the world, including its evil.   _____

_____ 17. Most suffering is brought about by man himself, as a consequence of moral failure.   _____

_____ 18. Man's moral failure is his own fault, not God's.   _____

_____ 19. Only science deals with what is real; what science neglects is imaginary and unreal.   _____

_____ 20. A scientist and a religionist can view the universe in the same way.   _____

_____ 21. All living things are organic and self-maintaining—that is, they consist of parts working together to preserve the whole organism and avoid injury and death.   _____

_____ 22. Creation is not a finished product but a process with an open future.   _____

_____ 23. Belief in God is necessary in order to understand both man and the universe.   _____

_____ 24. The universe operates by both natural and moral law, but there seems to be no connection between them—you can keep (or violate) one without being rewarded (or punished) by the other.   _____

THE LABORATORY MIDNIGHT

Science is what the world is, earth and water.
And what its seasons do. And what space fountained it.
It is forges hidden underground. It is the dawn's slow salvo.
It is in the closed retort. And it is not yet.

It looks up and counts the Perseids in August,
A fire from nowhere like signals overhead
And it looks for portents, as redmen on a hill,
In the white stream where Altair swims with the Andromedid.

Now you who know what to believe, who have God with you
By desk and bed, blue fire in the stove;
Whom the rains from the northeast alter but perfect
Into new powers, and new pities, and new love;

Go look in lava flows for newer elements,
And dismantle the electric shape of matter like a house;
And weigh the mountains in small sensitive scales;
Break buds; and test the senses of a mouse;

And if you are unpanicked, tell me what you find
On how the sun flies and the snow is spent,
What blasts and bessemers we live in, that dissolve
All the loam loaned to spine and ligament.

Reuel Denney

JUDAISM AND
SCIENTIFIC THOUGHT
Jack Bemporad

Modern science gives us a picture of the
universe which is in many ways congenial to
a religious world view.

IN *belief unbound,* W. P. Montague has written: "Religion as we shall conceive it is the acceptance neither of a primitive absurdity nor of a sophisticated truism, but of a momentous possibility—the possibility namely that what is highest in spirit is also deepest in nature, that the ideal and the real are at least to some extent identified, not merely evanescently in our own lives but enduringly in the universe itself. If this possibility were an actuality, if there truly were at the heart of nature something akin to us, a conserver and increaser of values, and if we could not only know this and act upon it, but really feel it, life would suddenly become radiant. For no longer should we be alien accidents in an indifferent world, uncharacterized by-products of the blindly whirling atoms; and no longer would the things that matter most be at the mercy of the things that matter least."

Montague's view of religion contains three concepts: meaning, order, and value. Religion is the assurance or the reassurance that life and the universe have meaning and that meaning is impossible without order attuned to values.

Religion as the quest for meaning is not an abstract or intellectual pursuit, but lies at the very depth of a person once he begins to ask himself about the purpose of existence. Religion is concerned with the ultimate beliefs that shape and justify one's life. The quest for religion begins when man searches for the meaning of his existence, when he seeks the purpose and significance of his life, and when he judges himself by values that go beyond his limited self. The religious quest begins with the self-questioning of the meaning and purpose of one's existence, and from one's own existence to the existence of all that is.

The question man ultimately asks himself is, Why is there something rather than nothing and what is the reason and meaning of the being that is? This question of meaning is never a factual question. It is not raised by asking what *is,* but rather by asking what *for,* why? It is a question inseparably connected with the value of one's life and of existence in general.

In his search for meaning, man has always tried to find support in the universe around him for the values he cherishes, for the good he strives to achieve. Until the modern era, man could find such assurance because his religious affirmations were in harmony with scientific and philosophical affirmations of the time. Throughout the Middle Ages, Jewish theologians succeeded in harmonizing Jewish tradition and Greek philosophy, most notably the philosophy of Aristotle. There was good reason for the success. It was based on a presumed similarity between Greek philosophy and Jewish thought. Both systems believed that God was a purely spiritual being, nonphysical and eternal, the object of devotion and absolutely unique. Furthermore, God was, for both systems, the ground for the order of the universe, for its goodness and intelligibility. Both systems emphasized the objective character of human values. Man was able to feel at home in the universe, he was in harmony with nature. Both the classical and Jewish heritages were one in affirming the centrality of God, the importance of the spiritual life, and the objective character of values. All of these gave man a definite place in the order of things.

With the emergence of physics in the sixteenth century, this harmony was shattered. It is a mistake to think that the rise of the new science was merely the introduction of a few new facts, like Galileo's doctrine of motion or Copernicus' heliocentric theory. The real transformation of the new science was that it produced a completely new and different view of reality and truth. What was certain and real for the new science was only what could be mathematically deduced. This led to the gigantic attempt to mathematize all experience in order to achieve certainty. The real world was viewed as a machine functioning according to mathematical laws. The only true method for its investigation was the mathematical method. With this idea in mind, Galileo said:

"Philosophy is written in the great book which ever lies before our eyes . . . the universe. But we cannot understand it if we do not first learn the language and grasp the symbols in which it is written. The book is written in the mathematical language and the symbols are triangles, circles, and other geometric symbols without whose help it is impossible to comprehend a single word of it, without which one wanders in vain through a dark labyrinth."

Galileo here describes a strictly mathematical, mechanistic universe, without reference to value or purpose. It is a universe that Whitehead described as "matter blindly running."

Mechanism soon extended itself to the domain of the self. As Neo-Darwinism triumphed, even man's rationality and understanding came to be seen as the last stage of a blind, accidental, and meaningless process. Whereas the man of the medieval world had viewed himself as the image of God and as the climax of the order and structure of a universe with a hierarchy of objective values, the man of the modern, scientific world could view himself only as a homeless, unintelligible entity in an unintelligible universe. He was a chance event, an accident in a blind world.

The ultimate paradox of scientific materialism, however, is that it affirms a chance universe, uncreated, valueless, purposeless, containing no values and meaning, and yet which accidentally and blindly gives rise to man—a caring, valuing, meaning-seeking being.

It makes very little sense to console man by telling him that despite the complete indifference of the cosmos he can still build a good life. If the good life is merely a projection, an illusion unsupported by nature and reality, then one can only be told to build a dream.

Science generalizes, idealizes, and abstracts from our overall experience, selecting from our experiences only those elements which can be mathematized. This abstraction ignores the greater part of experience. However, the scientist or philosopher of science errs when he makes the further judgment that only the experience science deals with is real and what it neglects must be either subjective or illusory. It is this dogmatic assertion of scientific materialism—that the real world is the world that the physicist constructs and that reality is only that which can be mathematized and measured so that only quantity is intelligible and all elements of quality and value are illusory—that presents a view of reality which has no place for religion. It is important to note that this is an attempt on the part of materialistic philosophy to identify the real with the mechanical and mathematical, and it is by no means a necessary consequence of scientific findings. On the contrary, it is our firm belief that this mechanistic doctrine is not only false but that it finds very little support in contemporary science. In fact, Werkmeister has said that "it contradicts the very spirit of science and should be discarded."

I do not maintain that contemporary science can provide a foundation for or justify a religious world view. But it does allow for the kind of world view that is *not opposed to the claims of religion*. The findings of contemporary science can be seen in a broader context that is not incompatible with religious affirmations.

All science presupposes being and order. It takes them for granted and does not discuss the more radical question of the ground for the being and order of what is.

We are struck with the questions: Why is there something rather than nothing and what is the ground of the being that is? Why is there order and not chaos and what is the ground of the order that is? These questions go beyond the scope and range of science. As Whitehead stated, order cannot be taken for granted.

"The order of the world is no accident. There is nothing actual which could be actual without some measure of order."

And again:

"It is not the case that there is an actual world which accidentally happens to exhibit an order of nature. There is an actual world because there is an order in nature. If there were no order, there would be no world."

Contemporary physics and biology maintain that there is something in every element of the universe which seeks satisfaction. This implies aim. Recent developments in physics, such as De Paule's exclusion principle, provide us with examples of aim and patterns of order even on the subatomic level that are unexplainable within the context of simple mechanics and force the physicist to introduce other criteria of self-organization on the level of subatomic physics. Once we consider the emergence of life, then we must take into consideration its self-maintaining quality. Organic systems tend to preserve themselves and are structured in terms of hierarchical order. This order is characterized by the emergence of more differentiated, more complex, levels of life. What all this leads to is, at first, an organic character to nature where the whole determines the parts and acts as a coordinating and unifying agent.

76

There is a hierarchical series of whole-part relations which are the result of emergence. Harris makes this clear when he states:

"Each of the prior phases sums up and sublimates in itself those which precede it. . . . The prior phases are not left behind nor utterly transcended, but are consolidated, sublated and comprehended in the developed form, which is their own developed form, not an alien addendum thrust upon them from above."

To say that this coordination is the result of matter blindly running or of an accidental effect is inconceivable and is only accepted by those who want to believe in mechanism and scientific materialism at all costs. It is with men that there emerges a new level with awesome and magnificent possibilities, a self-conscious being who can begin to understand and affect this process. Man strives for what transcends him, for the good, the true, and the beautiful. With the emergence of man, the whole development is radically affected and this concern of man must qualify the whole process. If man has been a blind result of an uncaring and meaningless process, then, as Hans Jonas states:

"The seeing is a product of the blind, the caring a product of the uncaring . . . Does not this paradox cast doubt on the very concept of an indifferent nature, that abstraction of physical science? . . . As the product of the indifferent, (man's) being, too, must be indifferent. Then the facing of his mortality would simply warrant the reaction, 'let us eat and drink for tomorrow we die.' There is no point in caring for what has no sanction behind it in any creative intention. But if in . . . facing our finitude, we find that we care, not only whether we exist but how we exist—then the mere fact of there being such a supreme care, anywhere within the world, must also qualify the totality which harbors that fact, and even more so if 'it' alone was the productive cause of that fact."

And when we speak of this totality which harbors supreme care and turn to the question of the "sanction behind it in a creative intent," we must go beyond the results of science, as amenable as they have been to man and his values. Man is the only being in nature that seeks to understand the whole and his place in it. He is concerned with truth and ethics and is aware through his reason that the process which could give rise to a being who could view truth and who could strive for justice could not be the result of shifting atoms but in some way at the very start the ground of all being must have harbored what found its realization in man.

Self-conscious man is aware of his values and goals, of his deepest needs and aspiration. Man asks, in the words of Whitehead, "What in the way of value is the attainment of life? And it can find no such value till it has merged its individual claim with that of the objective universe."

An objective universe, as we have seen, contains all those elements that scientific materialism discarded as subjective and illusory. Desire, self-organization, emergence, consciousness, thought have all been reintroduced as objective in a hierarchy of the nature of things. This new hierarchy differs from the medieval one in several respects.

The medieval world view understood nature as a hierarchical series of objective structures with their own intrinsic ends. This order was the direct creation of God. (The alternative to this view was seen to be what Whitehead called "matter blindly running.") The facts of contemporary science do not support the creation of a completed, static universe wherein everything is the result of divinely imposed law. Neither, however, do the facts give any foundation to the view that all occurs by chance through the mere shuffling of elements.

We must affirm the creation of a universe, but one that is unfinished, incomplete, and in the making. Creation, as Hartshorne has pointed out, must be the "creation of creators." There is both order and chance in the world, both being and becoming, law and freedom. But novelty makes risk, as well as loss and evil, real.

God created the universe with possibilities for life, mind, and value. Diversity and complexity and the desire for life in the animal realm become self-conscious in man. And with man, a new and stupendous vision comes into the world. It is the vision of God. Now, the good, the true, and the beautiful become goals to be achieved, ends to be realized. What Plato called the "forms" and Jewish tradition calls "Torah"—the pattern for creation—is envisioned as the logical and ethical ground for all things. The logical foundations are the ground for all possible being and order. The ethical task stands as the lure, the goal to be realized through man. Between logical order and moral achievement, stands nature—not the dead nature of scientific materialism, but a pulsating process, a whole-part hierarchy of the successive stages of emergence.

When man becomes aware of his place as the culmination of an unfinished process and recognizes that he is aware of values and truths which he strives to attain and embody—truths he does not legislate nor produce—then he can consider them as the foundation and the goals of his action.

It is due to God that there is something rather than nothing, order rather than chaos, the primacy of good and not the primacy of evil. Neither being nor order nor aim at value is intelligible, without some reference to God as creator, as the impetus to greater differentiation, organization, and harmony. But order is not all of a type. There is logical, natural, and moral order. Moral order is a goal to be achieved and not a fact. This indicates man's task. God must be such as to allow for man's task. In creating the world, God decided on the side of having man be the decider of his fate and not fate the arbiter of man's destiny.

It is a mistake to see creation as a finished product. Creation is a process with an open future. It is not the case that God creates a finished universe. God has created and is creating with His creatures a basically unfinished universe. The goal of creation is the actualization of an ideal order of things.

The fact of evil is the conclusive proof that there is an unfinished character to reality. Science deals with an ideally closed world. The laws of nature are there to be discovered. Religion deals with an essential unfinished world. Religion is concerned with what needs completion, with a universe-in-the-making. It must actualize the truths it stands for.

The ultimate solution to the problem of evil is the affirmation that being, with its risks and possibilities of loss, is better than nonbeing and nothingness; that time and temporality are real and not merely appearance. A perfect universe is a static universe.

God creates the formative elements and acts as the divine inspiration to man's task but God does not take on man's task. It is man that is to help and continue the process of creation and be a cocreator with God.

God is necessary for the continuity and the solidarity of the world. God sustains the world and works toward order in becoming. God is the basis and ground of the novelty of the world. Without God there is no reservoir of potentiality and becoming. God is not merely the foundation and ground of physical law but also the ground of the ideal vision without which there would be no advance but only mere repetitiveness. God is necessary for the universe and for man to be intelligible. Only through belief in God as creator and sustainer, as the ground of being and order, as the source of inspiration in worship, as the ground for the values man must realize—only through such a belief in God can man find meaning and value in his existence. Only then will the things that matter most not be at the mercy of the things that matter least. But what is highest in man will find a response in the God he seeks and worships.

TRY THESE PROJECTS FOR—
JUDAISM AND SCIENTIFIC THOUGHT,
by Bemporad

1. *Express yourself.*

■ Write an *Epitaph for Man*, to be engraved on an indestructible substance, and sealed in an indestructible shelter with a mechanism that automatically exposes it at the moment the last man on earth dies. Follow the usual tombstone format (Born . . . Died . . .) or design your own. You might briefly summarize man's accomplishments and/or failures, what difference his (brief? long?) existence has made to the universe, what his purpose was (or what he thought it was), and his final message to any other form of intelligent life that may arise (or arrive). Be as humorous or as serious as you wish. Your *Epitaph for Man* might make a striking poster or cartoon or a page in a class book for this unit.

■ Reread the creation story with which Russell begins the previous essay, then write your own version with Russell as a model, but the way you think Bemporad might have done it.

■ Write an imaginary dialogue between Bemporad and Russell, in which they reject each other's view of the universe; if you can, end with some things they both agree on. You may want your teacher and classmates to check out this dialogue, and then you may want to revise it and distribute it, post it, put it in the class book, present it, or tape it.

2. *Design and mount a bulletin board or poster display.*

Go through all the essays so far, including all the discussion questions, and underline key phrases that you think concisely express a clear position on an important point—whether you agree with that position or not. Print or type each such phrase on a separate 3 x 5 card, and mount these cards in four (or five) vertical columns, one for each author, so that cards suggesting agreement *or* disagreement with one another are on the same horizontal line. Border the disagreeing cards in red. Be ready, when you explain this display to the class, to say whether these authors tend to agree or disagree (proportion of plain to red-bordered cards); whether any one author generally disagrees with the others (does one column have most of the red-bordered cards?); and whether the ideas they agree on are more or less important than the ideas they disagree on (compare the problems raised or answered in the plain and the red-bordered cards).

3. *Review your Hebrew.*

Look up the Hebrew terms for important concepts in this unit. (Science, religion, faith, belief, creation, prayer, worship, etc.) Trace the etymological origin of each Hebrew term and compare with the etymological origin of the English term. For which concepts does the root word in both languages have the same meaning? For which concepts does the root word in each language have a different meaning? Make two separate lists to show or distribute to the class, and be ready to give any conclusions you can draw.

4. *Research.*

■ Erich Fromm and ethical humanists.

■ Christian Science—its view of the universe.

■ *The Devil and Daniel Webster*, by Stephen Vincent Benet, a magnificent short story which was also made into a play, a movie, and an opera.

■ The God of Jewish prayer—All-powerful or merely more powerful? (Resource: Specific prayers from the *Union Prayer Book*.)

After You Have Read—
JUDAISM AND SCIENTIFIC THOUGHT,
by Bemporad

Discuss these questions:

1. According to Bemporad, both religion and science accept this idea—meaning, order, and values are inherent in the universe, and they have an objective character and exist outside of man. How would previous authors in this unit (Townes, Einstein, Etkin, Russell) react to this statement? Considering the following statements, how did our talmudic sages view the idea that purpose, order, and values transcend man?

"The angels argued with God about creating man. 'Peace' and 'Truth' were opposed to creating man, since he would constantly war with his fellow man and try to deceive him. But 'Love' favored the creation of man, since he would love his fellow man and cherish him." (*Genesis Rabbah* 8:5.)

"The Torah was God's 'blueprint' for creating the world." (*Tanchuma Bereshit* 1, 6b.)

2. Read carefully the hymn *Adon Olam*. Then answer these questions:
   Was there meaning, purpose, or value in the universe before the creation or evolution of man?
   If human life disappears, will there still be meaning in whatever is left? What if both human and animal life vanish? What if all living things die out?
   Would God still exist if the entire universe were destroyed?

3. Voltaire said: "If God did not exist, it would be necessary to invent him." Did he mean God does not exist except in man's imagination? God's existence is so necessary it would be impossible to conceive of the universe without Him?
   From this statement was Voltaire an atheist or a theist?

4. Ask yourself this question: What difference does it make to me personally, to Jews, to Judaism, to mankind, which of the following three basic ideas I accept about the reality of values:
   Values are part of the entire universe, and are therefore part of man.
   Values are part of man, but not of the universe around him.
   Values are part of man, and man is part of the universe, therefore values are also part of the universe.

5. Consider these two statements:
   "Being (existence) cannot come from nonbeing by chance." (Bemporad.)
   "It is not the case that there is an actual world which accidentally happens

82

to exhibit an order in nature. There is an actual world because there is an order in nature. If there were no order, there would be no world." (Whitehead.)

Test this idea against your everyday experience:

When you talk, read, and write, are you using a language that accidentally happens to have sense, meaning, purpose? Or is it a language because it has sense, meaning, purpose? And if it didn't, it wouldn't be a language?

Does any natural development (the birth of a child, for example, or his growth into maturity) accidentally happen to have an order, or does the development take place because there is an order, without which there would be no development?

What do the words "accident," "accidental," "accidentally" mean? You could have an orderly system in which an accident could take place and break its orderliness (you can sprain an ankle and not get to school or work as planned). But could you have an accident that was not a breaking of some orderly structure? (Would it be "accidental" to sprain an ankle that was never actually strong enough to support you and get you wherever you planned to go?)

Now reread the Bemporad and Whitehead statements above. Considering the actual facts of our everyday experience, do you agree that chance or accident can prevent or interrupt an orderly process, but can never create or cause it?

6. Given the following assumption, which of the possible conclusions do you accept, and why?

Assumption: Scientific observation affirms law and order in the universe.

Conclusions: There must be a force or intelligence responsible, which we call "God."

There may be such a force or intelligence.

There may not be such a force or intelligence.

7. Take a new look at the what-is-what-ought-to-be distinction between science and religion. Is it accurate? Too limited? Too broad?

Do scientists also sometimes consider what ought to be? How about a doctor, a researcher seeking a cancer cure, a designer of life-support systems for astronauts?

Does science have two aspects? Describing, analyzing, classifying (what is); and controlling, changing, redirecting (what ought to be)?

Do religionists also deal with what is? War, poverty, persecution, and so on?

Does religion have two aspects? Recognition of what is; and moving us closer to what ought to be?

React to the following distinction:

Science deals with problems, ways of solving them, ways of testing proposed solutions, ways of using the solutions to deal with still other problems, solve them, test their solutions, use their solutions to deal with still other problems.

Religion deals with our attitudes and feelings about problems, about ways to solve, test, use, etc.

"Right" and "wrong" in science has to do with getting what you want or avoiding what you don't want—you simply ask, Does it work or doesn't it work?

"Right" and "wrong" in religion has to do with approving or disapproving what you want or don't want—something can work for you and be "wrong," it can work against you and be "right."

Example: Science tackles the questions of getting a man to the moon and back all in one piece. "Right" means you do, "wrong" means you don't. Religion tackles the question of wanting to get to the moon in the first place. "Right" means we should want to, "wrong" means we should not want to.

Try this approach out on other examples of your own.

8. According to Bemporad, there is so much scientific support for order and purpose in the universe that a universe of chaos and accident "is really inconceivable." In fact, he adds, such a universe "is accepted by those who want to believe in mechanism and scientific materialism at all cost." The charge here is that believers in chaos and accident want to believe it so badly that they ignore all scientific evidence against it.

Could he be thinking of Russell in the previous essay? Check back over that essay, and agree or disagree with each of the following statements:

Russell does not mention or try to refute any of the scientific evidence against his position.

Townes, Einstein, Etkin, and Bemporad offer scientific evidence for their position.

Russell offers no scientific evidence for his position; he merely states his position as so obviously correct it must be taken for granted.

Both sides first take a position, then find evidence for it, ignore evidence against it.

Both sides first carefully examine evidence, pro and con, and then arrive at a reasoned conclusion.

9. Express in your own words Bemporad's concept of God. Decide whether you agree or disagree with it after considering the following questions:

What are the assumptions, premises, and arguments on which this concept is based?

Does the concept follow logically from these assumptions, premises, and arguments?

Is it the only concept that could logically follow them?

Does he deal with the concept of a *personal* God, who cares about man and responds to prayer?

According to his concept, is prayer valid? What kind of prayer? What purpose would public worship have?

What would Einstein have thought of Bemporad's God?

10. Look back at the "Before You Read" questions for this essay, where you wrote yes or no as a modern rabbi and a modern scientist might answer for each statement. Skip every statement where you put two yeses or two noes or two question marks (where you have the same answer from both the rabbi and the scientist). Check off every statement where you put yes in one column and no in the other, or a question mark in one column and a yes or a no in the other (the rabbi has a different answer from the scientist).

Suppose you *had* to have the same answer in both columns, how would you change each statement you have checked—to two yeses or two noes or two question marks? Be ready to explain why in each case you chose the alternative you did—why two yeses instead of two noes, and so on.

Now, match wits with the editors of this course: We would have written the same answer, on both sides of every statement. For us, the modern rabbi and the modern scientist would agree every single time. What do you think we'd have put for each statement—two yeses, or two noes, or two question marks? Why do you think so?

Ask Yourself Again

After you've finished Part I, "Science and Theology," go back over all the "Before You Read" sections. Reconsider your answers, and write out questions, statements, or answers, ideas—as many as you like—under these headings:

1. I've changed my mind about—

2. I still feel the same way I did before about—

3. I feel more certain than before about—

4. I feel less certain than before about—

Some suggested steps to follow at the conclusion of every unit.

■ Collect from fellow students all "Ask Yourself Again" sections (or copies of these sections, if they prefer).

■ Prepare a tally sheet on this order:

Question	Changed their mind	Still feel the same way	More certain about	Less certain about

■ From classmates' papers, copy out each question or statement under "Question," and put a tally mark (/) under one of the headings, as indicated on each paper. When another paper has the same questions, just add tally marks in the right column. If a new question appears on the paper, copy it out under "Question" and keep tallying it every time it is mentioned again.

■ Add up your tallies in each column, and put the whole thing on large poster board or mimeograph it—but this time give the questions in order from most to least; first the question on which the most students changed their minds, then the question with the next smaller number of students changing their minds, and so on. If you think of a better or clearer way to organize your tallies, go right ahead. If you want to do a superjob, go through all the "Before You Read" sections and collect questions that nobody mentioned at all—questions everybody ignored, or forgot, or wasn't interested in.

■ Finally, draw some conclusions (if you're supermathematical, base them on percentages). So far in this unit how much mind changing? Reaffirmation of original opinion? Increase of certainty? Increase of doubt? In which of these has the unit so far been most worthwhile? Least worthwhile? Perhaps you'd like to lead a class discussion criticizing and evaluating the unit so far—and then send a letter about the results to the editors.

Part II

TECHNOLOGY AND RELIGIOUS VALUES

BEFORE YOU READ—

THE
TECHNOPHILIACS,
by Ferry

Label each of the following facts about modern technology.

"G" means in general good for our lives; "NG" means in general bad for our lives; "?" means you're not sure.

_____ 1. Chemical and physical agents exist that can change a person's mental or emotional makeup.

_____ 2. Subliminal advertising flashes a "buy" message on a movie or tv screen too fast for you to notice consciously, but such repeated flashes make you unconsciously ready to buy the flashed brand or product when you see it in a store.

_____ 3. As a result of space exploration, men can now land on the moon.

_____ 4. Nuclear power is becoming available to more nations all the time.

_____ 5. DDT, a new "miracle" insect killer invented about twenty-five years ago, is one of our cheapest and most effective pesticides.

_____ 6. A few years ago, a drug named thalidomide was invented as a tranquilizer especially for epileptics.

_____ 7. Our store of knowledge is increasing at the rate of 500,000 pages a minute. In order to "keep up," the average scientist will soon have to give one full day a week to formal education.

_____ 8. Increasing speed is one result of modern technology. For example: Air travel has revved up since man's flight in 1903 from 6 m.p.h. to 25,000 m.p.h. A machine given one sample of blood can print out the results of 12 different chemical tests in just 12 minutes. An experimental washing machine washes, dries, and irons a bedsheet in 45 seconds. Another machine can print *all* of Shakespeare's plays in a little over one minute—or 60,000 letters a second. Processing the quarterly earning reports of $3\frac{1}{2}$ million companies takes, by the latest methods, 100 days; a new optical scanner can do it in 8 hours.

_____ 9. All the world's legal codes and international agreements can be fed into a computer, available for instant recall by anyone at any time. Some lawyers already use such a computer.

10. By the year 2000, when you will probably still be alive, people will be able to do such things as preselect their children's sex; regenerate defective or damaged organs; preserve sperm and egg cells of superior men and women, and use them to create new life long after those men and women have died; live 90 or 100 years in good health; "reprogram" body cells to end inherited diseases like hemophilia or acquire new traits like higher intelligence; inject, erase, or change memories; change a person's sex at will.

11. Eighty per cent of all the world's scientists who ever lived are living now.

12. Germ warfare is a military possibility today.

LINES WRITTEN AFTER THE DISCOVERY
BY THE AUTHOR
OF THE GERM OF YELLOW FEVER

This day relenting God
Hath placed within my hand
A wondrous thing; and God
Be praised. At His command,

Seeking His secret deeds
With tears and toiling breath,
I find thy cunning seeds,
O million-murdering Death.

I know this little thing
A myriad men will save.
O Death, where is thy sting?
Thy victory, O Grave?

Ronald Ross

RICHARD TOLMAN'S UNIVERSE

Eddington's universe goes phut.
Richard Tolman's can open and shut.
Eddington's bursts without grace or tact,
But Tolman's swells and perhaps may contract.
All that Eddington can see
Is entropy, entropy, entropy.
But Tolman throws a punch to the jaw
Of the second thermodynamic law.
His heart, indeed, is comforted
When he sees a displacement toward the red,
And he at once sets up an equation
Which wholly alters the situation.
Give more rope! Give more rope!
Give more rope to the spectroscope.
Then catch Andromeda and hang her.
Tolman's a first-chop Doppleganger.
Tell me what Newton never knew,
Things about Messier 42.
In words of one syllable display
How Cepheid variables get that way.
Bring the criminal to the bar,
That stripped the atoms of Van Maanen's star.
Let me hear alpha particles clank.
Serve my electrons on a Planck.
And, no matter what sort of Hell has popped,
Let not the constant h be dropped.
For things grow nebulous to me,
Especially the nebulae.
Astrophysics is perfectly grand.
There's nothing in it I understand
Except that I'm stuck for better or worse
In Tolman's elastic universe.

Leonard Bacon

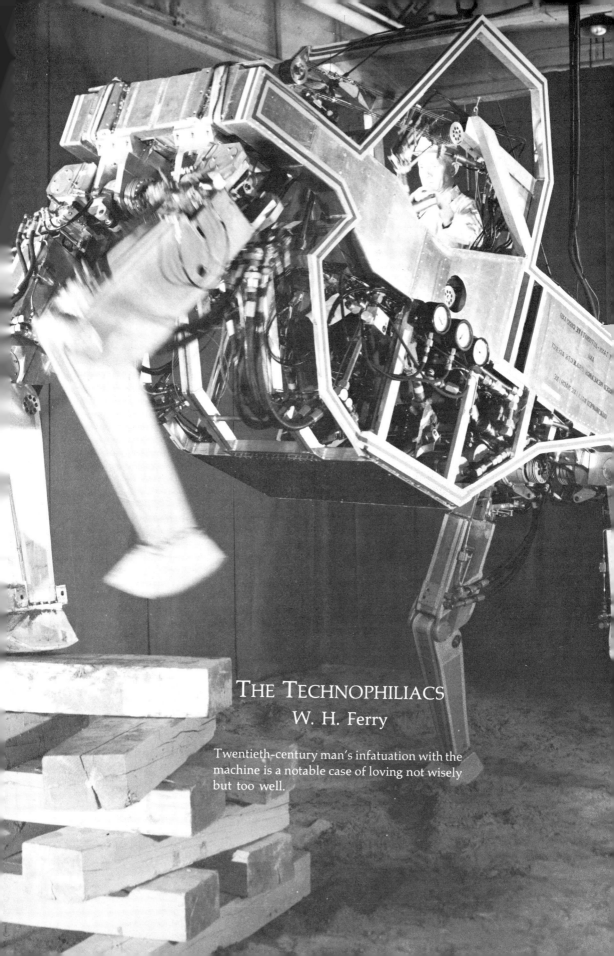

THE TECHNOPHILIACS
W. H. Ferry

Twentieth-century man's infatuation with the
machine is a notable case of loving not wisely
but too well.

I AM NOT a noble savage or a Luddite. I do not wish to live in the forest, hunt for my supper, or weave my own turtleneck sweater. I do not wish to break up the machines, yank the telephone wire out of the wall, or ride a horse to City Hall. I am respectful of the accomplishments of technology, though not of all of them and not all the time. I do not think that technology can be dispensed with, or halted in its tracks, nor would I wish to do so.

Yet I see a wave of fedupness gathering in the land. It is fedupness with the pretensions, practices, and encroachments of technology. It is not a very big wave, but it is gaining strength and will soon, I hope, have to be taken into consideration by all the social weatherwatchers, whether in the shrines of technology or in the corridors of government.

I detect this rising tide of fedupness in books and learned tracts, which agitate about matters as apparently remote from one another as the gradual asphyxiation of Los Angeles, the manipulation of human sentiments by advertisers, and the elimination of jobs by cybernation. I detect it in worries about the plight of the cities, which are turning into divided camps as full of destitution and fear as they are of elegant technology. I detect it in the growing apprehension that we have become a people resplendent in means and depleted in purpose.

The accepted modern equation is this: science and technology equal progress and human welfare. The statement seems to me doubtful, considering the world around us. I see technology as a semi-autonomous phenomenon, at present winning a struggle with humanity because of the unreasoning reverence with which it is regarded. Thus, I see the necessity for a more rational attitude, which may be expressed in the phrase, People first, Machines second. For I sense that fedupness comes mainly from the feeling that human concerns are being steadily displaced by the pursuit of technique.

I adopt Jacques Ellul's definition of technology (in *The Technological Society*): "the ensemble of practices by which one uses available resources in order to achieve certain valued ends." This definition includes all techniques—those of bureaucracy and propaganda as well as those of machines and processes. I believe that current history supports Ellul's observation that "technique evolves apart from man's intentions, following its own intrinsic processes, independent of external forces or human aims." Yet I do not think that this has to be the case. Nor for that matter does Ellul, who declares that there are three possible ways to break up the inexorableness of the processes he describes. The first is nuclear war. The second is the direct intervention of God. The third is that an increasing number of people will become aware enough of the threat of technology to assert their freedom by "upsetting the course of this evolution."

My argument henceforth depends on the third possibility—the possibility that we can do something about it if only we decide to do so.

I would like to see technology slowed down and directed to the benefit of mankind. The liberation of mankind is not the automatic result of technology, though its rapt idolators claim that it is. I would like to see technology placed under regulation so as to minimize the human sacrifices that are an inevitable cost of its development. I would like to see the great capacities of technology brought to bear on the problems of this bewildering age. These capacities now exhibit themselves in such giddy and senseless adventures as the supersonic transport plane, the space race, ever more obscene military hardware, and the manufacture of the maximum number of vehicles that Detroit can force into the economy of the nation, with social and psychic effects beyond calculation.

I believe, in short, that we have to take time to stand back and see what we want to do with ourselves as human beings. What kind of community do we wish to make of ourselves as a nation and, far more important, as one small portion of the international community of men? In such an appraisal technology will play a great part, for its capabilities run to bringing us together as surely as they run to blowing us apart.

But it is hard to persuade Americans that technology either has much to do with the dilemmas facing them or that it threatens to bind and strangle humanity. Even to decide on the test I recommend—that of People first, Machines second—will require a most unlikely act of political determination by Americans. For one of the curious characteristics of technology is that it is the object of the piety of industrial man. Modern man venerates formulas, the gadgetry of outer space and terrestrial conflict as well as the gadgetry of the hobby shop and the home, the techniques of managing one another as well as the techniques of caring for one another. The veneration is explicable, for behind it is a theological justification: science and technology, it is said in profound error, emerge from God's injunction to Adam to subdue the earth and tame its creatures and compel its resources to the uses of man.

Another curiosity about technology is its unilateral thrust—its onewayness, so to speak. It appears to offer no options except to do whatever can be done. If it is possible to zoom to Venus, let us hasten there at once. If it is possible to develop an educational machine to replace the schoolroom, let us get at it instantly. If it is possible to refine electronic sorcery to seduce citizens into purchases they cannot afford or votes they should not cast, who will say nay?

Still another peculiarity of technology is that no one is responsible for its excesses. No one doubts that the techniques of modern warfare involve moral issues. The ability to kill a nation and extinguish a culture is both a technological fact and a moral problem. But whose problem, and how is it to be formulated? A good deal of piffle has been written about the "unfair" college students who have attempted to keep representatives of the war business off campuses, whether they are recruiters for the Marines or for Dow Chemical. Little dialogue is possible between the conscientiousness of the napalm-maker and the moral conscience of the students. These young people may be boisterous and disturbing; but they know about the moral issue, even if they may present it in confusing or inept terms. In the early 1940s the German universities were doubtless besought to provide more efficient ways of burning up such enemies of the German state as the Jews. If there was a moral issue in Nazi Germany then, there is a moral issue in the situation on our campuses now. We should rejoice in the student who is willing to bring it to public attention. No one, I think, will argue that providing more efficacious human furnaces—a better burn for a buck—is the proper business of universities, and has no odor of immorality attached to it. The analogies in U.S. universities are uncomfortable and real.

An equally compelling illustration is furnished by the engineers of the new biology, with their well-publicized dreams of improving the race by the manipulation of genes. Dr. Catherine Roberts, a microbiologist, sounds the warning: no biologists know enough to attempt any such thing.

"The crucial point here seems to be what criteria are used in evaluating the superior humanness of an outstanding individual," she says in *The Scientific Conscience.* ". . . positive eugenics might conceivably be able to raise the intelligence quotient of man and to alter his physical state; yet I cannot believe that these are the essential criteria of becoming more human. A mere increase in the proportion of the healthy superintellectuals will not suffice for future human progress, for in the absence or neglect of love and virtue, such 'outstanding' individuals will never be more human than we. . . . The positive eugenists, despite their earnest intentions, know nothing—absolutely nothing—about the genetic base of love and virtue, and it is misleading to the world at large even to include such traits in a prospectus of their policy.

"The moral philosophy, the art, the music, and the literature which constitute most of the superior knowledge of our cultural heritage have no place in the scientist's laboratory. . . . Is not the world outlook derived from it more humanly significant than the objective world outlook of science? Would it not be the height of folly to permit contemporary biologists to control and direct the further development of human life?"

The moral issues adduced by Dr. Roberts need no amplification. Other examples are not so stark, and the issue is presented in a more subtle way.

Despite the repeated foul-ups of technology all along the line—the fatal error of thalidomide, the daily irony of 450 horsepower cars on 12-mile-per-hour streets—the illusion persists that technology proceeds from triumph to triumph. Thus it is not generally appreciated that Lake Erie, for example, was killed by mere bad technology, by the failure to measure the lake's phosphate outflow. It was an example of high criminal neglect. But whose neglect? Even the aircraft magnates who have been given many millions of tax dollars to perfect the supersonic transport had to admit recently that they really did not know what they were doing when they won the government contract. It turned out that the machine they had designed would not be able to zip over the ocean at supersonic

94

speeds after all—at least with passengers. The budding SST could carry fuel or passengers, it turned out, but not both. So it is back to the computers for a year or more. The delay should not be regretted; it provides a sobering-up period to reconsider whether we really want to go ahead with this folly merely because we can, or think we can.

It will be said that man has always defiled his environment, has always misused natural resources, and that we are merely witnessing more of the same today. This is a spurious argument. Historically it is only half-true. The analogy fails because never before did man's degradation of his environment reach out to nature itself and threaten the ecological web of which we are all strands.

It is tempting to expand on the theme of ecological disaster: the ruined waterways, oxygen-free air, annihilated wild life, and the dwindling resources and rising waste that rampant technology produces. But, important as it is, this is a more or less familiar tale. Less noticed but more significant are the alienating effects of technology. Men are simply being separated from themselves, insulated from the earth and the mysteries. Alienation is no exotic plant that grows and is to be seen only in the psychoanalyst's parlor. There is, to use but one example, Dr. Robert Rieff's warning that the nightwatchman of today is the model of tomorrow's workman, who will neither labor nor make, but only look at dials and graphs. When a man's only chore is to watch for the red light indicating trouble, there must be some destructive effect on his sense of workmanship, some deep hurt to his ego. This is alienation. This is the toll of the quantified society. Thomas Huxley almost a century ago asked the classic question as he reflected on what he and his fellow scientists were doing: "The great issue about which hangs a true sublimity and the terror of overhanging fate is, what are [we] going to do with all those things?"

I feel no need to point out the benefits conferred by technique, for everyone does this. I come down hard on its malevolent results and potentialities because I believe it is far more than coincidence that the high point of technical development and the low point in national morale should occur together. There is not much joy in the land. At the height of physical power the nation shivers with insecurity. Generation battles generation; black battles white; work loses its savor; contentment, ease, and simple human satisfaction disappear. We are a rich, aging, vain, despairing nation. Our condition makes me wonder whether Ferry's Second Law does not apply to nations as well as to individuals: money never improved anybody.

The surrogate for such old-fashioned emotions as contentment or simple satisfaction may be called technophiliasm, translatable as "enraptured by technique." A technophiliac is that enthusiastic human combination of slide rule and computer who believes that anything that can be done must be done, anything that can be measured needs to be measured. The archetypal technophiliac is to be found in science fiction. He is the odd-looking object festooned with tubes and wires to be found on the command deck of Galaxy-Gertie XII, off on another quasar hunt, frozen stiff for the light years of his voyage and replaced from time to time by a similarly anonymous and efficient biomechanical link. The technophiliacs are interchangeable, and since they have few recognizable human emotions they may really be the men of the future that they like to be called.

I conclude that technology has to be brought under public regulation and direction. I do not know quite how to do this, for it is an extraordinarily complicated undertaking. It cannot be done piecemeal, because technique is in a constant state of overspill, one development always setting in motion long rivers of other results. Indeed, it may rightly be asked whether planning on the scale required is at all possible. Our creaking political machinery, fashioned for another era, appears to be unable to deal with overriding national questions such as that of the ghetto. How can the antiquated political apparatus, then, be expected to limit the toxic developments of technique? Yet the basic question remains, and it is not how we can become more efficient but how we can become more human. Among other things this means less centralization, not more—the participation of citizens in decisions that closely touch them. How this can be done in a system that is more and more comprehensive in its approach is only one of the significant and unresolved problems in political theory. Yet we must try; and even if the effort in the long run should fail—even if technology and its proponents showed themselves to be beyond human control—the effort would still have been worthwhile. For the argument about the primacy of decent and humanity-enhancing potentials of technique would open the eyes of a public that has thought of it largely in terms of costly weapons systems or gee-whiz space probers, and seldom in terms of its crippling aspects. They would at least learn there should be a choice, let us say, between becoming the master of technology or its passive slave, between becoming technophiliacs and becoming ever more human. That choice may be what Clifton Fadiman describes as "the many perfectly solid pleasures Megalopolis will offer: three-dimensional tv, instant information, instant communication, instant sex, 24-hour sports spectacles, almost instantaneous change of locations, and synthetic food." But I do not think that this would be the choice, because where these conditions most nearly obtain today is where the greatest weariness of spirit is to be encountered. I would even suggest that the public quest for wisdom about the human uses of technology might revivify the country. It would be an exciting, spirit-stirring discussion. It might supply the common purpose and interests we are acknowledged to lack.

Great hazards would also attend the quest. What if it should be decided that we have all the technology we need to meet the reasonable requirements of humanity, and that all that is really wanting is the political devices to put it to our service? Suppose people should suddenly realize that they are just plain bored, fed up with a superplenty of technology and its so-called fruits?

What if people just stopped buying things, disregarded the advertisements and the commercials, decided, even for a while, against the second television set, the new kitchen, the thinginess of modern life? This latter speculation need not depend on the search for the control of technology. It might happen anyway: people might decide, as a change, to sit in the sun, and watch the birds, and talk.

I repeat that I do not want to do away with technique. I am in favor of automation, and cybernation, and computers, and scientists poring over their tables. I do not wish to destroy the technophiliac's fun and games, only attach them to honorable human enterprises. I favor all the help that technique can give in unloading tasks from man that are unworthy of human labor. If our cities are to be unriddled, the unriddling will have to be done by technology, and I know it. I am merely in favor of first things first—People first, Machines second—machines in the service of man, not vice versa.

Asher Lans put his finger on the sore spot. "The wonder world of the technocrats subjects the industrial society to virtually uncontrolled decision-making by experts and technicians," he wrote in *The American Scholar*. "It minimizes the area of effective politics and therefore popular control over the decision-making process. The traditional institutions of parliamentary democracy and a judicial structure invented to preserve formal political freedom need supplementation by new tools of government if we are to limit . . . political arbitrariness and economic injustice in an age of nation-wide planning."

This is to say that technology affects the person and the common life more intimately and often than does any government, federal or local; yet it is against the aggrandizement of government that we are constantly warned. I can conceive of no way of effectively regulating and dispersing the power of technology other than by constitutional authorization.

The country is committed to industrialization, as it was committed at birth to representative government. The parallel is awkward but important. The issue then was balancing the rights of minorities with those of majorities, and an intricate federal structure was built on this concern.

The cosmos of the new technology is a complex and unpremeditated structure. Planning, authorized and given its duties and limitations in a revised constitution, is the only method I can see for providing that the structure be kept to human dimensions. Planning on this scale and legitimized by the constitution would take a very long time to achieve. On the other hand, several developments are making ever more feasible planning on the national and international scale now required, without having to wait for a revised constitution. One is the growing appreciation of the necessity for a system of social accounts "which would indicate the social benefits and social costs of investments and services. . . . In such an approach, production and innovation would be measured, not simply in terms of its profitability to an individual or a corporation, but in relation to how it affects the society—of its profitability from the standpoint of the common good." These words are *obiter dicta* from an influential presidential commission that reported in 1966 on the impact technology is having on employment.

Another development is the rapid increase in the arts of technological forecasting. A study of such activity for the Organization for Economic Cooperation and Development was begun under the impression that only a rudimentary start at technological prediction had been made. However, the results of the study cover more than 400 pages, cite experiments in technological forecasting in more than a dozen countries, and conclude rather breathlessly that the "information [on this topic has] expanded virtually to the exploding point." These predictions are made for a variety of reasons—scholarly, governmental, or industrial.

A final development is the expanding sophistication of the planning mechanisms already in use. The United States, like every other industrial society, lives by plans. They are for the most part plans put together by private interests for their own advantage. But one result is that familiarity with the idea and the procedures of planning is becoming widespread.

No one has offered a satisfactory explanation of the internal disquiet afflicting the land. As good an explanation as any, in my judgment, is guilt and uncertainty about the misuse of our resources—about the misuse of fellow human beings as well as of nature and its mysteries. Perhaps it is centered in what has been called the "ecological conscience," which Thomas Merton describes elsewhere in this issue. This is one of the most important moral discoveries of our time, this exposure of a "dependence on a balance which [man] is not only free to destroy but which he has already begun to destroy."

The ecological conscience has been excluded from the technological surge. Planning, however expert, that does not take as its first principle the promptings of the ecological conscience can only result in more misery and soul-wrenching and alienation for new generations. As Robinson Jeffers wrote, ". . . the greatest beauty is organic wholeness, the wholeness of life and things, the divine beauty of the universe."

I realize that this may be read as a homily on the times as much as a message on technology. But they cannot be separated. My bias is plain; I think that technophiliasm is taking us toward disaster. I feel sorry for technophiliacs. My prescriptions may be unpleasant; but I do not think that I have misdiagnosed the common condition. I hope fedupness with the *hubris* of the technologists grows and grows, for technique is disintegrating and demoralizing the community.

The facts and the possibilities, both tonic and toxic, are there for all to see. We still have time to make choices for humanity—not much time, but some.

Admiral Rickover has the final word: "Humanistically viewed, technology can have no legitimacy unless it inflicts no harm. Granted this premise, the prerequisite for users of technology is—or ought to be—that they comprehend and respect the laws of science applicable to their particular technology; and, should it be potentially harmful, that they abstain from using the technology until they have found ways to render it harmless."

In short, People first, Machines second.

TRY THESE PROJECTS FOR—
THE TECHNOPHILIACS,
by Ferry

---

1. *Express yourself.*

◼ Make fun of technophilia (technology-worship) by composing a satirical hymn—to a computer, for instance.

◼ Think up slogans for signs to carry at an anti-technology (or pro-technology) demonstration. (Example: "We demand more . . . ." or "We're fed up with . . . .") Make the signs but consult your teacher and rabbi before planning on actually using them. (For example: Where would you demonstrate? Against whom?)

◼ Illustrate seriously or satirically in cartoons some of the "horrible examples" in this essay. (For example: Gradual asphyxiation of Los Angeles, traffic jams, death of Lake Erie, etc.)

◼ Check the *New York Times Index* for a recent news item on ecology, conservation, technology, air or water pollution, destruction of natural resources, drug hazards, etc., and write an imaginary interview with the authority quoted in the news report, beginning with his answers to questions the reporter must have asked him, then going on to your own additional questions and his (imaginary) answers.

2. *Act out, or make a single concept film, filmstrip, slide set, or tape recording.*

◼ A new (imaginary) federal law requires every new invention to pass an Ethics and Morals board before it can be patented and manufactured. Simulate discussions and decisions of this board on the following two (actual, not imaginary) inventions submitted to it. One makes it possible to use lightning to regulate the distribution and amount of rainfall over a given area; the other makes it possible to deflect lightning from one area onto another. The two inventors should be present, to give all possible utilizations—agricultural, military, etc.

◼ Simulate the jury's decision and verdict following an actual homicide trial that took place a few years ago in Belgium.

Defendants: A young mother, her husband, mother, sister, and family doctor.

Charge: Killing her one-week old baby girl.

Facts of the killing (proved in court and admitted by the defendants): The family decided to kill the baby. The doctor gave them a prescription for enough barbiturates to kill an infant. The mother mixed the barbiturates with the baby's honey-sweetened formula, and the baby died. The baby's suspicious pediatrician tipped off the police, who caught the mother with the dead baby still in the house, and found in the medicine chest a drug called thalidomide.

Motive: The pregnant mother, like thousands of others, had taken thalidomide, a drug developed in West Germany for epileptics that seemed to be "the perfect sleeping pill," with no chance of overdose and none of the usual side-effects. But the babies born to such mothers were horribly crippled and deformed. The murdered baby in this case had no arms, her face was disfigured, and her anal canal emptied into her vagina. The family and their doctor felt the baby was better off dead.

Defendants' plea: Letting the baby live would have been far more cruel and far more criminal. The mother said she had asked about artificial limbs for the baby, but had been told they could not be fitted in this case. She added: "If only my baby had also been mentally abnormal, she would never have realized her fate. But she had a normal brain. She would have realized—she would have known." The defense attorney asked for acquittal, blaming "a poisoned gift from modern science."

Prosecutor's plea: The only question before the jury was whether or not the defendants had knowingly committed the crime they were charged with. The evidence and the defendants' own admissions showed that they had. Murder—the willful taking of human life—is a legal and moral crime in all civilized societies of all times. No human being has the right to take another's life, whatever the reason. It's not up to us to determine who should live and who should die. The prosecuting attorney demanded conviction, but recommended leniency in punishment.

Jury's decision and verdict: . . . ? (For the actual verdict, see page 103.)

■ Act out a meeting of college students who are considering what action to take about military recruitment on their campus and/or college involvement in development of military weapons. Include in the group a chairman; an "observer"; students for and against opposing college policy; students for and against demonstrations, sit-ins, violence if necessary; faculty members for and against both these positions; a scientist and/or technologist or two; a rabbi. (On the last role, better consult your own rabbi first, for a realistic background; you may also want to consult a real scientist or technologist too.) The chairman of the meeting should see to it that three things happen:

All possible choices and alternatives are considered.

A decision is reached to approve some alternatives and reject others.

The approved alternatives are arranged in priority order—what action first, what action second if the first fails, and so on. (End the meeting here without going into details of how to actually carry out each action.)

The "observer"—you, a small committee, your teacher, or your rabbi—who has taken no part at all in the discussion now evaluates it—strong and weak arguments; good and bad decisions; and especially parts in the discussion played by science or technology, the parts played by religious, moral, ethical ideas.

3. *Get action.*

■ Draw up a carefully worded resolution, either generally on technological dangers or specifically on one destructive trend, urging action by the federal, state, or local government.

A formal resolution has two parts:

Paragraphs, beginning with "Whereas . . ." and stating reasons for composing and submitting the resolution.

Paragraphs, beginning "Be it therefore resolved, that . . ." and stating the specific actions the authors of the resolution want taken.

Send copies of your resolution to the President of the United States, your governor, or your mayor; to the appropriate cabinet member or department head; to your own community's senators, congressmen, state legislature, etc.; to newspapers and to tv and radio stations.

Get lots of help and advice on this, from your instructor, rabbi, and others. And be sure to include religious, moral, and ethical concerns as well as physical and mental ones. Identify your congregations and class clearly, also your instructor, and all members of the class should sign.

■ Find out what programs and activities of your own synagogue could be classified as countertechnological—that is, developing personal freedom, responsibility, and growth; preventing alienation and depersonalization; strengthening the humane qualities of members' lives, etc. Consult your rabbi, synagogue officers and committee chairman, temple bulletins and reports, etc.

■ Write to a national synagogue organization—the Union of American Hebrew Congregations, the United Synagogue of America, etc.—for bulletins and brochures describing (a) its own progress and activities, and (b) those of individual congregations throughout the country. Compile a list of countertechnological programs and activities going on elsewhere but not in your own congregation. Add to this list some ideas of your own and of your fellow students. Write, visit, or invite to your class the president of your congregation to express to him your appreciation of what the congregation is doing, and to urge other things for it to do. Try to get a definite commitment to at least one new step, and follow up at a reasonable time to see how it has worked out.

4. *Go creative.*

■ Ferry mentions three ways that the threat of technology might be stopped or controlled: nuclear war, direct intervention by God, more people recognizing the threat and demanding action against it. But he deals only with the third way. So you look into the other ways—one or both—by assuming that it happens, and figuring out what probably would happen afterward.

Write about it, illustrate it, or tell about it five, ten, twenty-five, fifty or 100 years after the event, in the form of a diary or captions for photographs, or briefing "visitors from another planet."

■ Invent a technology game—with a board, counters, moves, etc. Players start off with an invention, then move forward or back or lose turns according to how much money it makes, how many people it helps or hurts, etc.

■ Make up a list of new inventions that mankind needs for a better life. Think of food, clothing, shelter. Look at a daily newspaper, and you'll find plenty for modern technology to correct.

5. *Research.*

■ How human is an animal—and vice versa? Read *The Naked Ape,* by Desmond Morris; *The Magic Animal,* by Philip Wylie. Draw some conclusions, with evidence and examples.

■ Does man love freedom or fear it? Read *Escape from Freedom* and/or *The Revolution of Hope,* both by Erich Fromm, and report on (a) the author's basic thesis, (b) the ethical principles he stresses, (c) how these principles are related to Judaism.

■ Are we destroying ourselves? Read one or more of the following, and set down their major ideas—*Silent Spring,* by Rachel Carson; *Ecology,* by Eugene P. Odum; *Man in Nature,* by Marston Bates; *Science and Survival,* by Barry Commoner; *The Technological Society,* by Jacques Ellul. How does the author agree or disagree with Ferry?

■ Ecology—its meaning, history, principles, demands.

■ Human problems today, and what's being done (or not done) about them.
Pollution, air or water. (How did Lake Erie "die" and how is Lake Superior doing?)
Subliminal advertising—What it is, who wants it, how it works; is it legal, moral, ethical; what are its chances.
Cybernation and automation—pros and cons, attitudes of organized labor, moral/ethical issues, possible solutions.
Urban crises—racial, health, educational, transportation, crime, etc.; common factors underlying all the various upheavals; what can be done; will things get better or worse; why most people stay in the big cities, and some even move back.
Loss of purpose—alienation, depersonalization, helplessness, hopelessness.

Jury decision (Project 2, page 101): After one week's trial, a jury of 12 men took just 105 minutes to reach a verdict of *not guilty.*

AFTER YOU HAVE READ—
THE TECHNOPHILIACS,
by Ferry

Discuss these questions:

1. What is the relationship between science and technology? How do they resemble each other, differ from each other, depend on each other?

   The following statement by Ellul may help you get started.

   "Everyone has been taught that technique is an application of science; more particularly (science being pure speculation), technique figures as the point of contact between material reality and the scientific formula. But it also appears as the practical product, the application of the formulas to practical life.

   "This is a false view. Historically, technique preceded science; even primitive man was acquainted with certain techniques. But technique did begin to extend itself only after science appeared; to progress, technique had to wait for science.

   "In the present era, the border between technical activity and scientific activity is not at all sharply defined. The majority of investigators in a laboratory are technicians who perform tasks far removed from what is commonly imagined to be scientific work. Pure science seems to be yielding its place to an applied science which now and again reaches a brilliant peak from which new technical research becomes possible. Scientific activity has been superseded by technical activity to such a degree that we can no longer conceive of science without its technical outcome." (Ellul, *The Technological Society*, pp. 7–11.)

2. According to Ferry (and Ellul) technology is not limited to machines, but includes all techniques—standardized ways of achieving a desired result. What does "standardized" mean in this definition? What are some examples in our lives today of techniques other than machines? (An example to start you off: College entrance exams.)

3. Give examples from your own personal life that corroborate Ferry's statement that "human concerns are being steadily replaced by the pursuit of technique."

4. Ellul mentions three ways to halt "the pretensions, practices, and encroachments of technology." Ferry deals, he says, with the third way only. Why do you suppose he ignores the other two ways? Do you agree that these two ways need not or cannot be discussed? Your reasons?

5. Is the following statement valid?

   For nontechnological solutions to the ills of technology, we must look to traditional institutions that have always been life-creating and humanity-preserving. For Jews, for example, such an institution could be the synagogue.

As a *bet ha-knesset*, a house of assembly, the synagogue could provide programs that permit greater self-expression and help to enhance human life against the impact of the machine.

Is this function of the synagogue feasible?

Should it be a function of the synagogue?

If so, what new forms, rituals, programs, activities would have to be tried? What changes in present programs?

What are other life-creating, humanity-preserving traditional institutions in our lives? Are they strong or weak? Growing stronger or growing weaker? What can we do to strengthen them and utilize them for curing the ills of technology?

6. Think of some recent inventions that fit each of these headings:

   Helps and does good only, causes no harm whatever.

   Can help or harm, depending on how it's used.

   Can only do harm, does no good whatever.

   Is it ever right to suppress the first kind? When this happens, what is probably the motive behind it? What should be done about the second kind; and why, how, by whom? About the third kind?

7. Industrial firms plan many years ahead. For example, paper companies have figured out that in the year 2000 they'll need at least twice as much paper as today. So, for several years now, they have had experts at work breeding seedlings for trees that will grow faster, resist disease, and produce more and better pulpwood.

   Do our synagogues and religious schools plan this far ahead? Foresee the needs of the next generation and try to get ready now to meet them then?

   Think of some significant change in the way people will probably live in 2000. For example: We will probably work at home more, using visiphones, computers, facsimilizers, and other electronic devices to transact business, hold conferences, get information, and so on, and will probably travel more and faster and more often in our leisure time.

   How might this affect our synagogues and religious schools? What could they do now to be ready to deal with such a change then?

8. Scientific research and experimentation have found out two things about violence and vandalism:

   They are increasing sharply, among our middleclass whites as well as elsewhere in our population.

   They are greater in the larger cities; and so are apathy and indifference to them.

   Think of all the reasons you can why violence and vandalism keep increasing, and why the bigger the city the worse they are. Is there a connection?

Why should middleclass whites—who are not poor, underprivileged, uneducated, or mistreated—be just as guilty as others?

Think of all the remedies you can. Are they political, economic, scientific and technological, educational? Is there a religious answer?

9. Go back to the "Before You Read" section for this essay and look at the questions you labeled "NG" or "?" and try to figure out how they might be handled to lean more toward the "G" side.

This day of automation—Imagine:
Apollo's chariot dashing across
The sky to the nearest
Service station.

Wolffe Nadoolman, age 12

IT ROLLS ON

This is the time of wonder, it is written;
Man has undone the ultimate mysteries.
(We turn from the Chrysler Tower to watch a kitten,
Turn to a dead fish from Isocrates;
Drinkers on five day boats are gladly smitten
Unconscious on the subjugated seas;
Einstein is even more dull than Bulwer-Lytton;
You cannot smoke on the Los Angeles.)
Science no longer knows the verb-form "can't."
Fresh meat will soon be shipped by radio;
Scholars are harnessing the urgent ant
And making monstrous bastard fruits to grow,
Building machines for things I do not want,
Discovering truths I do not care to know.

Morris Bishop

BEFORE YOU READ—

CAN
TECHNOLOGY
REPLACE
SOCIAL
ENGINEERING?
by Weinberg

Study the following problems.

Which of the two solutions offered is the best (label it "1"); which is second best (label it "2").

1. The population explosion.
   _____ Persuade or force people to have fewer babies.
   _____ Distribute free or very cheap birth control devices that are easy, safe, and certain.

2. Race riots.
   _____ Educate people, or pass laws requiring them to get along together, be fair to one another, show no discrimination, and help one another out in every possible way.
   _____ Install free air conditioners and tv sets in every slum or "ghetto" home, on the theory that riots occur mostly on hot summer days, and these appliances will keep people comfortable at home and off the streets.

3. Auto accidents, deaths, and injuries.
   _____ Conduct educational campaigns, courses, tv/radio/movie programs, posters, etc., to encourage better driving habits and skills.
   _____ Make safer cars, roads, and streets.

4. When the U.S., to relieve severe famine in India, sent over tons of surplus wheat, some rice eaters there preferred to starve rather than eat anything else.
   _____ Send teachers, social workers, psychologists to persuade these people to learn to eat wheat as well as rice.
   _____ Send crop experts, chemicals, and equipment to increase rice production and develop new strains of rice that will grow faster and resist drought and disease better.

5. Poverty.

 _____ Start a social revolution to overthrow the profit system and social- ize all production so as to divide everything equally among all people.

 _____ Increase production so greatly there will be more than enough of everything to go around for everybody.

6. War.

 _____ Unite all nations into a single world government, similar to the American federal-and-state system, which would have one world army and separate world powers with certain powers reserved for the separate nations.

 _____ Create military weapons so powerful and efficient that there is simply no rational alternative to world peace.

7. Water shortage.

 _____ Persuade or educate people to use less water and not to waste it so much, and to live in less crowded regions with more water re- sources.

 _____ Find cheaper ways to get water from the oceans.

8. Personal unhappiness.

 _____ Have courses and clinics, books and pamphlets, lectures, programs to help people learn to control or express themselves, deal with their problems, improve their relationships with other people.

 _____ Invent a pill that automatically reduces anger, anxiety, insecurity.

9. Urban traffic jams.

 _____ Keep more cars out of cities and off certain streets, build more ex- pressways and parking lots, increase parking fine restrictions, raise bridge and tunnel tolls (especially for one-passenger cars).

 _____ Introduce automatic traffic controls and better, faster, cheaper, more comfortable public transportation in the form of monorails, air-pressure-driven subways, hydrofoil river boats.

10. Automation replacing workers.

 _____ Slow the process down, through restrictive laws or labor union strikes.

 _____ Find fast new ways to retrain workers.

11. The American textile industry has trouble competing in world markets because of higher costs due to our higher standard of living.

 _____ Increase government subsidies to textile firms and tariffs on im- ported textiles.

 _____ Install high-speed electronic computers in textile factories to lower costs.

12. Commuting between job and home.

_____ Get people to live near where they work.

_____ Promote "instant communication" devices so that more people can work at home yet be in instant touch with anyone or any group, any office or library, visually as well as aurally, with facsimile reproduction devices, contact with computers and information "banks," etc.

13. Home burglaries.

_____ Distribute posters, ads, messages to keep reminding people of basic rules to protect their homes, such as locking doors and windows, leaving a light on when away, canceling the paper and milk delivery when on vacation.

_____ Invent an inexpensive tamper-proof lock with an automatic alarm system connected with the nearest police station.

Can Technology Replace Social Engineering?

Alvin M. Weinberg

Can we identify Quick Technological Fixes for profound and almost infinitely complicated social problems—"fixes" that are within the grasp of modern technology, and which would either eliminate the original social problem without requiring a change in the individual's social attitudes, or would so alter the problem as to make its resolution more feasible?

D URING THE WAR, and immediately afterward, the federal government mobilized its scientific and technical resources, such as the Oak Ridge National Laboratory, around great technological problems. Nuclear reactors, nuclear weapons, radar, and space are some of the miraculous new technologies that have been created by this mobilization of federal effort. In the past few years there has been a major change in focus of much of our federal research. Instead of being preoccupied with technology, our government is now mobilizing around problems that are largely social. We are beginning to ask what we can do about world population, the deterioration of our environment, our educational system, our decaying cities, race relations, poverty. President Johnson has dedicated the power of a scientifically oriented federal apparatus to finding solutions for these complex social problems.

Social problems are much more complex than are technological problems, and much harder to identify: How do we know when our cities need renewing, or when our population is too big, or when our modes of transportation have broken down? The problems are, in a way, harder to identify just because their solutions are never clear-cut: How do we know when our cities are renewed, or our air clean enough, or our transportation convenient enough? By contrast the availability of a crisp and beautiful technological solution often helps focus on the problem to which the new technology is the solution. I doubt that we would have been nearly as concerned with an eventual shortage of energy as we now are if we had not had a neat solution—nuclear energy—available to eliminate the shortage.

There is a more basic sense in which social problems are harder than are technological problems. A social problem exists because many people behave, individually, in a socially unacceptable way. To solve a social problem one must induce social change—one must persuade many people to have fewer babies, or to drive more carefully, or to refrain from disliking Negroes. By contrast, resolution of a technological problem involves many fewer individual decisions. Once President Roosevelt decided to go after atomic energy, it was by comparison a relatively simple task to mobilize the Manhattan Project.

The resolution of social problems by the traditional methods—by motivating or forcing people to behave more rationally—is a frustrating business. People don't behave rationally; it is a long, hard business to persuade individuals to forego immediate personal gain or pleasure, as seen by the individual, in favor of longer-term social gain. And indeed, the aim of social engineering is to invent the social devices—usually legal, but also moral and educational and organizational—that will change each person's motivation and redirect his activities to ways that are more acceptable to the society.

The technologist is appalled by the difficulties faced by the social engineer; to engineer even a small social change by inducing individuals to behave differently is always hard even when the change is rather neutral or even beneficial. For example, some rice eaters in India are reported to prefer starvation to eating the wheat we send them. How much harder it is to change motivations where the individual is insecure and feels threatened if he acts differently, as illustrated by the poor white man's reluctance to accept the Negro as an equal. By contrast, technological engineering is simple; the rocket, the reactor, and the desalination plants are devices that are expensive to develop, to be sure, but their feasibility is relatively easy to assess, and their success relatively easy to achieve once one understands the scientific principles that underlie them.

It is therefore tempting to raise the following question: In view of the simplicity of technological engineering, and the complexity of social engineering, to what extent can social problems be circumvented by reducing them to technological problems? Can we identify Quick Technological Fixes for profound and almost infinitely complicated social problems, "fixes" that are within the grasp of modern technology, and which would either eliminate the original social problem without requiring a change in the individual's social attitudes, or would so alter the problem as to make its resolution more feasible? To paraphrase Ralph Nader, to what extent can technological remedies be found for social problems without first having to remove the causes of the problem? It is in this sense that I ask: "Can technology replace social engineering?"

THE MAJOR TECHNOLOGICAL FIXES OF THE PAST

To explain better what I have in mind I shall describe how two of our most profound social problems—poverty and war—have in some limited degree been solved by the Technological Fix, rather than by the methods of social engineering.

The traditional Marxian view of poverty regarded our economic ills as being primarily a question of maldistribution of goods. The Marxist recipe for elimination of poverty, therefore, was to eliminate profit, in the erroneous belief that it was the loss of this relatively small increment from the worker's paycheck that kept him poverty-stricken. The Marxist dogma is typical of the approach of the social engineer. One tries to convince or coerce many people to forego their short-term profits in what is presumed to be the long-term interest of the society as a whole.

The Marxian view seems archaic in this age of mass production and automation, not only to us, but apparently to many East European economists. For the brilliant advances in the technology of energy, of mass production, and of automation have created the affluent society. Technology has expanded our productive capacity so greatly that, even though our distribution is still inefficient and unfair by Marxian precepts, there is more than enough to go around. Technology has provided a "fix"—greatly expanded production of goods—which enables our capitalist society to achieve many of the aims of the Marxist social engineer without going through the social revolution Marx viewed as inevitable. Technology

113

has converted the seemingly intractable social problem of widespread poverty into a relatively tractable one.

My second example is war. The traditional Christian position views war as primarily a moral issue: If men become good, and model themselves after the Prince of Peace, they will live in peace. This doctrine is so deeply ingrained in the spirit of all civilized men that I suppose it is blasphemy to point out that it has never worked very well—that men have not been good, and that they are not paragons of virtue or even of reasonableness.

Although I realize it is a terribly presumptuous claim, I believe that Edward Teller may have supplied the nearest thing to a Quick Technological Fix to the problem of war. The hydrogen bomb greatly increases the provocation that would lead to large-scale war, not because men's motivations have been changed, nor because men have become more tolerant and understanding, but rather because the appeal to the primitive instinct of self-preservation has been intensified far beyond anything we could have imagined before the H-bomb was invented. To point out these things today, with the United States involved in a shooting war, must sound hollow and unconvincing; yet the desperate and partial peace we have now is far better than a full-fledged exchange of thermonuclear weapons. One can't deny that the Soviet leaders now recognize the force of H-bombs, and that this has surely contributed to the less militant attitude of the USSR. And one can only hope that the Chinese leadership, as it acquires familiarity with H-bombs, will also become less militant. If I were to be asked who has given the world a more effective means of achieving peace—our great religious leaders who urge men to love their neighbors and thus avoid fights, or our weapons technologists who simply present men with no rational alternative to peace—I would vote for the weapons technologist. That the peace we get is at best terribly fragile I cannot deny; yet, as I shall explain, I think technology can help stabilize our imperfect and precarious peace.

THE TECHNOLOGICAL FIXES OF THE FUTURE

Are there other Technological Fixes on the horizon, other technologies that can reduce immensely complicated social questions to a matter of "engineering"? Are there new technologies that offer society ways of circumventing social problems and at the same time do not require individuals to renounce short-term advantage for long-term gain?

Probably the most important new Technological Fix is the intra-uterine device for birth control. Before the IUD was invented, birth control demanded the very strong motivation of countless individuals. Even with the pill, the individual's motivation had to be sustained day in and day out; should it flag even temporarily, the strong motivation of the previous month might go for naught. But the IUD, being a one-shot method, greatly reduces the individual motivation required to induce a social change. To be sure, the mother must be sufficiently motivated to accept the IUD in the first place, but, as experience in India already seems to show, it is much easier to persuade the Indian mother to accept the IUD once than it is to persuade her to take a pill every day. The IUD does not completely replace social engineering by technology. Indeed, in some Spanish-American cultures where the husband's manliness is measured by the number of children he has, the IUD attacks only part of the problem. Yet in many other situations, as in India, the IUD so reduces the social component of the problem as to make an impossibly difficult social problem much less hopeless.

Let me turn now to problems which, from the beginning, have had both technical and social components—those concerned with conservation of our resources: our environment, our water, and our raw materials for production of the means of subsistence. The social issue here arises because many people by their individual acts cause shortages and thus create economic, and ultimately social, imbalance. For example, people use water wastefully, or they insist on moving to California because of its climate. And so we have water shortages; or too many people drive cars in Los Angeles with its curious meteorology, and Los Angeles suffocates from smog.

The water resources problem is a particularly good example of a complicated problem with strong social and technological connotations. Our management of water resources in the past has been based largely on the ancient Roman device, the aqueduct. Every water shortage was to be relieved by stealing water from someone else who at the moment didn't need the water or was too poor or too weak to prevent the theft. Southern California would steal from Northern California, New York City from upstate New York, the farmer who could afford a cloud-seeder from the farmer who could not afford a cloud-seeder. The social engineer insists that such expedients have gotten us into serious trouble; we have no water resources policy, we waste water disgracefully, and, perhaps, in denying the ethic of thriftiness in using water, we have generally undermined our moral fiber. The social engineer, therefore, views such technological shenanigans as being shortsighted, if not downright immoral. Instead, he says, we should persuade or force people to use less water, or to stay in the cold middle-west where water is plentiful instead of migrating to California where water is scarce.

The water technologist, on the other hand, views the social engineer's approach as rather impractical. To persuade people to use less water or to get along with expensive water is difficult, time-consuming and uncertain in the extreme. Moreover, say the technologists, what right does the water resources expert have to insist that people use water less wastefully? Green lawns and clean cars and swimming pools are part of the good life, American style, and what right do we have to deny this luxury if there is some alternative to cutting down the water we use?

Here we have a sharp confrontation of the two ways of dealing with a complex social issue: The social engineering way which asks people to behave more "reasonably," the technologist's way which tries to avoid changing people's habits or motivation. Even though I am a technologist, I have sympathy for the social engineer. I think we must use our water as efficiently as possible, that we ought to improve people's attitudes toward the use of water, and that everything that can be done to rationalize our water policy will be welcome. Yet, as a technologist, I believe I see ways of providing more water more cheaply than the social engineers may concede is possible.

I refer to the possibility of nuclear desalination. The social engineer dismisses the technologist's simple-minded idea of solving a water shortage by transporting more water, primarily because in so doing the water user steals water from someone else—perhaps foreclosing the possibility of ultimately utilizing land now only sparsely settled. But surely water drawn from the sea deprives no one of his share of water. The whole issue is then a technological one: Can fresh water be drawn from the sea cheaply enough to have a major impact on our chronically water-short areas like Southern California, Arizona, and the eastern seaboard?

I believe the answer is yes, although much hard technical work remains to be done. A large program to develop cheap methods of nuclear desalting has been undertaken by the United States, and I have little doubt that within the next ten to twenty years we shall see huge dual-purpose desalting plants springing up on many parched sea coasts of the world. At first these plants will produce water at municipal prices. But I believe, on the basis of research now in progress at Oak Ridge and elsewhere, water from the sea at a cost acceptable for agriculture—less than ten cents per one thousand gallons—is eventually in the cards. In short, for areas close to the sea coasts, technology can provide water without requiring a great and difficult effort to accomplish change in people's attitudes toward the utilization of water.

The Technological Fix for water is based on the availability of extremely cheap energy from very large nuclear reactors. What other social consequences can one foresee flowing from really cheap energy eventually available to every country, regardless of its endowment of conventional resources? While we now see only vaguely the outlines of the possibilities, it does seem likely that from very cheap nuclear energy we shall get hydrogen by electrolysis of water, and thence the all-important ammonia fertilizer necessary to help feed the hungry of the world; we shall reduce metals without requiring coking coal; we shall even power automobiles with electricity, via fuel cells or storage batteries, thus reducing our world's dependence on crude oil, as well as eliminating our air pollution insofar as it is caused by automobile exhaust or by the burning of fossil fuels. In short, the widespread availability of very cheap energy everywhere in the world ought to lead to an energy autarchy in every country of the world, and eventually to an autarchy in the many staples of life that should flow from really cheap energy.

116

WILL TECHNOLOGY REPLACE SOCIAL ENGINEERING?

I hope these examples suggest how social problems can be circumvented or at least reduced to less formidable proportions by the application of the Technological Fix. The examples I have given do not strike me as being fanciful, nor are they at all exhaustive. I have not touched, for example, upon the extent to which really cheap computers and improved technology of communication can help improve elementary teaching without having first to improve our elementary teachers. Nor have I mentioned Ralph Nader's brilliant observation that a safer car, and even its development and adoption by the automobile industry, is a quicker and probably surer way to reduce traffic deaths than is a campaign to teach people to drive more carefully. Nor have I invoked some really fanciful Technological Fixes: like providing air conditioners, and free electricity to operate them, for every Negro family in Watts on the assumption, suggested by Huntington, that race rioting is correlated with hot, humid weather—or the ultimate Technological Fix, Aldous Huxley's "soma pills" to eliminate human unhappiness without improving human relations in the usual sense.

My examples illustrate both the strength and the weakness of the Technological Fix for social problems. The Technological Fix accepts man's intrinsic shortcomings and circumvents them or capitalizes on them for socially useful ends. The fix is therefore eminently practical and in the short term relatively effective. One doesn't wait around trying to change people's minds: If people want more water, one gets them more water rather than requiring them to reduce their use of water; if people insist on driving autos while they are drunk, one provides safer autos that prevent injuries even in a severe accident.

But the technological solutions to social problems tend to be incomplete and metastable, to replace one social problem with another. Perhaps the best example of this instability is the peace imposed upon us by the H-bomb. Evidently the *pax hydrogenium* is metastable in two senses: In the short-term, because the aggressor still enjoys such an advantage; in the long-term, because the discrepancy between have and have-not nations must eventually be resolved if we are to have permanent peace. Yet, for these particular shortcomings, technology has something to offer. To the imbalance between offense and defense, technology says let us devise passive defense which redresses the balance. A world with H-bombs and adequate civil defense is less likely to lapse into thermonuclear war than a world with H-bombs alone, at least if one concedes that the danger of thermonuclear war mainly lies in the acts of irresponsible leaders. Anything that deters the irresponsible leader is a force for peace: A technologically sound civil defense would therefore help stabilize the balance of terror.

To the discrepancy between haves and have-nots, technology offers the nuclear energy revolution, with its possibility of autarchy for haves and have-nots alike.

How this might work to stabilize our metastable thermonuclear peace is suggested by the possible political effect of the recently proposed Israeli desalting plant: I should think that the Arab states would be much less set upon destroying the Jordan River Project if the Israelis had a desalination plant in reserve that would nullify the effect of such action. In this connection, I think countries like ours can contribute very much. Our country will soon have to decide whether to continue to spend 5.5×10^9 per year for space exploration after our lunar landing. Is it too outrageous to suggest that some of this money be devoted to building huge nuclear desalting complexes in the arid ocean rims of the troubled world? If the plants are powered with breeder reactors, the out-of-pocket costs, once the plants are built, should be low enough to make large-scale agriculture feasible in these areas. I estimate that for 4×10^9 per year we could build enough desalting capacity to feed more than ten million new mouths per year, provided we use agricultural methods that husband water, and we would thereby help stabilize the metastable, bomb-imposed balance of terror.

Yet I am afraid we technologists will not satisfy our social engineers, who tell us that our Technological Fixes do not get to the heart of the problem; they are at best temporary expedients; they create new problems as they solve old ones; to put a Technological Fix into effect requires a positive social action. Eventually, social engineering, like the Supreme Court decision on desegregation, must be invoked to solve social problems. And of course our social engineers are right: Technology will never replace social engineering. But technology has provided and will continue to provide to the social engineer broader options, making intractable social problems less intractable; perhaps most of all, technology will buy time, the precious commodity that converts violent social revolution into acceptable social evolution.

Our country now recognizes—and is mobilizing to meet—the great social problems that corrupt and disfigure our human existence. It is natural that in this mobilization we should look first to the social engineer. Unfortunately, however, the apparatus most readily available to the government, like the great federal laboratories, is technologically, not socially oriented. I believe we have a great opportunity here for, as I hope I have persuaded the reader, many of our social problems do admit of technological solutions. Our already deployed technological apparatus can contribute to the resolution of social questions. I plead, therefore, first for our government to deploy its laboratories, its hardware contractors, its engineering universities, on social problems. And I plead secondly for understanding and cooperation between technologist and social engineer. Even with all the help he can get from the technologist, the social engineer's problems are never really solved. It is only by cooperation between technologist and social engineer that we can hope to achieve what is the aim of all technologists and social engineers—a better society, and thereby a better life, for all of us who are part of society.

TRY THESE PROJECTS FOR—
CAN TECHNOLOGY REPLACE SOCIAL ENGINEERING?
by Weinberg

1. *Choose any of the following technological devices that interest you, find out how they work, and then list all the ways you can think of in which each device could be used.*

■ In Jewish worship.

■ In synagogue and/or religious administration.

■ In religious school classrooms.

Devices

computer	programmed learning
videotape	facsimile reproduction
multimedia	telelecture
short circuit tv	telephone conferences

2. *Now, list the gains and losses you predict from using the device, and decide whether, on balance, there would be more gain or more loss. You can present your results in different forms.*

■ Poster or chart.

■ Statement pro or con; or pro-and-con.

■ Letter or resolution urging the proper authorities in your congregation to introduce the device—or, if they're already using it, to stop using it.

■ Description of an imaginary "technologized" worship service or classroom lesson—serious, to show gains; satirical, to show losses.

3. *Organize a political campaign on "Our future and who should control it?"*

The campaign should be complete with platform, speeches, slogans, a final class vote.

■ The government? Federal, state, or local?

■ Committees of technologists and/or social engineers? Who appoints or selects them?

■ Large national or international organizations? Business? Labor? Foundations? Universities? Religious? The U.N.?

■ Democratic processes through popular votes?

■ Or—???

4. *Go creative.*

■ Write up your diary for an imaginary day without any technological device—no alarm clock, car, telephone, etc.; make clear whether it is a "good" or a "bad" day for you.

■ Find and read a poem by Carl Sandburg called *Prayer of Steel* and write an original poem or paragraph of your own in which a technological device "prays" for its own "destiny." Make your title simply "Prayer," try not to mention the device itself, and challenge classmates to figure out what device you had in mind.

■ Compose a "biography" of some technological device, old or new or imaginary—its "birth," its "take-over," of human life, its benefits and/or dangers, its "death."

■ "The Future I Want" (or Don't Want)
It could be:
A straightforward essay or editorial.
A "Letter to Humanity" or "To My Descendants."
A poem, a short story, or a conversation between two people of the future.
Drawings, cartoons, or a comic strip.
A bulletin board display of news clippings, magazine articles, photographs, original writings and drawings.

5. *Get action.*

■ In your synagogue.
Find out about a specific project being conducted or planned by your congregational Committee on Social Action or Interfaith or Israel.
Think of some way you, individually, or a class committee, or the entire class, could help carry out this project.
Arrange with the committee chairman to carry out your proposed part of the project.

■ Write to your own state senators and district congressmen asking about U.S. chemical and biological warfare programs.
Their unnecessary secrecy.
The stockpiling of material potentially highly dangerous.
Permanent or irreparable damage to the environment in Vietnam.
Safety practices in laboratories working with chemical and biological warfare agents.
Safety practices in transporting such agents across the country.
Research contracts with academic and private institutions.
When (and if) you get answers, discuss, post, and publicize them.

6. *Research.*

■ Consult the *Reader's Guide to Periodical Literature* in your neighborhood library for the latest three or six month period, to compare the number of articles listed under "Technology" with the number listed under "Religion."

Find and read one or two of the articles listed under each subject. Does an article on one topic mention the other topic? Note down ways that the articles you read agree or disagree with Weinberg; also any interesting new ideas or examples you find.

■ Find out how social and technological changes are sponsored.

By the Ford Foundation (or any other large foundation) through grants of money to communities, scientists, and others.

By any well-known university, or institute of technology, through research projects.

■ Read *The Organization Man*, by William Whyte, listing its main points, and an example from your own everyday life that either proves or disproves the point.

■ Select some past technological development, prehistoric, ancient, or medieval, such as a tool, manufacturing or agricultural technique, utilization of a natural resource, etc. Report on how it changed human life, and whether for good or bad or both. Any lessons to be learned for our own day?

■ Jews have always been numerically outstanding in achievement, in scientific professions like medicine, mathematics, and others. Get some statistics on this, and two or three distinguished individual examples from ancient, medieval, and modern times. Can you discover, or suggest for yourself, any reasons for special Jewish eminence in scientific work?

After You Have Read—
CAN TECHNOLOGY REPLACE SOCIAL ENGINEERING?
by Weinberg

Discuss these questions:

1. This essay contrasts two approaches to social problems.

   Social engineering—motivating or forcing people to behave differently or assume different attitudes; in essence, adjusting people to fit the situation.

   Technological fix—a technological change that eliminates the problem without requiring people to adjust their attitudes or their behavior; or changes the problem so that it is easier to solve; or improves conditions without even dealing with the causes of the problem.

   For each of the following, think of two possible procedures: (a) one that fits the definition of social engineering, and (b) one that fits the definition of technological fix.

   Physician treating an alcoholic, a drug addict, or an overweight person.

   a. _____ b. _____

   Parent with a child afraid of the dark.

   a. _____ b. _____

   Teacher with a pupil who can't spell.

   a. _____ b. _____

   Judge sentencing a juvenile delinquent.

   a. _____ b. _____

   A businessman whose employees make too many mistakes.

   a. _____ b. _____

   Which solution, (a) or (b), seems in each case faster, easier, cheaper? Which kind of solution, (a) or (b), do you think wiser to seek?

2. Find an example in the article—or one of your own—of a technological fix and provide the particular social problem this fix has solved completely; has solved in some limited degree; has prevented its worsening so as to give us more time to deal with it; has helped with; has created or intensified.

3. Do you agree that weapons technologists who simply present man with no rational alternative to peace have done more for world peace than great religious leaders who urge men to love their neighbors and thus avoid fights? Has religion ever been a force for peace between nations? Between racial groups within a city?

4. The intra-uterine device is an example of a technological fix. Does this device, in your opinion, do more good than harm, or vice versa?

5. Our country faces grave internal problems that require huge sums of money to deal with—deterioration of our environment, crisis in education, decaying

cities, poverty. Are we justified in spending so many billions of dollars on space exploration and lunar landings? Spell out your answer concretely in terms of the probable gains from each program, and how these gains balance out.

6. Modern life is dominated by huge organizations in government, business, education, and so on. Give the reasons whether this is good for us and if so why we should welcome it; if it is necessary whether we like it or not; and whether it is bad for us and we should resist it.

7. Every major technological development produces "spin-offs"—new inventions, or techniques that can be applied to a completely different technological need. Some examples are microwave radar (from television), the pictophone or visiphone (from man-made satellites), and even nonstick frying pans. Space travel has already given us, and is expected to give us much more, new techniques for improving living conditions here on earth in all sorts of ways.

Do such spin-offs justify a technological step which might otherwise not be justifiable—like space exploration?

Are spin-offs likely from investment in social problems here on earth, like poverty, pollution, urban crises?

Should space exploration, with all its spin-offs, be curtailed, and the money go to social problems where there might be no spin-offs? Why or why not?

8. One reason the State of Israel has been able to defend itself so decisively against the larger and more numerous Arab states is its unusually high level of scientific and technological development.

The United States, too, has enemies throughout the world, some of them large and powerful and pressing forward in military technology as fast as they can.

Is investment in military technology justified in a nation under attack by enemy nations?

Is it justified in a nation in peacetime if other nations, possibly hostile, are engaging in it?

Does an "arms race"—competition between hostile nations to keep up or get ahead in military technology—increase or decrease the chance for war?

If it increases the chance for war, why do nations do it?

If it decreases the chance for war, why do most people and most nations talk fearfully of military "escalation" and hopefully about "disarmament"?

9. In May, 1969, the U.N. secretary general, U. Thant, issued the following statement:

". . . unless the countries of the world subordinate their ancient quarrels and launch a global partnership to curb problems of military arms, human environment, population, and others, a major crisis looms ahead . . . The world has only ten years left before its problems reach staggering proportions . . . beyond our capacity to control."

Do you agree with him? If so, what do you think can be done about it, and by whom?

Fill in below.

Ten years from 1969 is 1979. The year I am reading this is _____, and the situation has (improved) (worsened) (stayed just as bad). I recommend immediate action by _____

to _____ .

Especially I urge synagogues and other Jewish organizations to _____

10. Look back at the "Before You Read" section for this essay. Notice that all the first solutions are those of social engineering, and all the second solutions are those of technology. If Weinberg filled in this section, what would he have checked?

INNATE HELIUM

Religious faith is a most filling vapor.
It swirls occluded in us under tight
Compression to uplift us out of weight—
As in those buoyant bird bones thin as paper,
To give them still more buoyancy in flight.
Some gas like helium must be innate.

Robert Frost

124

AVODAT HALEV

"Lord God of test tube and blueprint,

*"Who jointed molecules of dust and shook them till their name
was Adam,*

"Who taught worms and stars how they could live together,

*"Appear now among the parliaments of conquerors and give
instruction to their schemes;*

*"Measure out new liberties so none shall suffer from his
father's colour or the credo of his choice:*

*"Post proofs that brotherhood is not so wild a dream as those
who profit by postponing it pretend:*

*"Sit at the treaty table and convoy the hopes of little
people through expected straits,*

*"And press into the final seal a sign that peace will come
for longer than posterities can see ahead,*

"That man unto his fellow man shall be a friend for ever."

Norman Corwin

ENTROPY

*Matter whose movement moves us all
Moves to its random funeral,
And Gresham's law that fits the purse
Seems to fit the universe.
Against the drift what form can move?
(The God of order is called Love.)*

Theodore Spencer

Ask yourself:

If you had the power, like Frankenstein, to create and control a human life, to produce "the ideal human being," what would your creature be like? Describe him.

1. Physically.

2. Mentally.

3. Emotionally.

4. Morally.

5. His job, occupation, profession.

6. His recreation, pastimes, hobbies, interests.

7. His interests in or attitudes toward art, music, literature, theatre, tv, sports.

8. His interest in or attitude toward sex, marriage, children, family.

9. His interests in or attitudes toward:
   Religion. (Would he be *Jewish?*)
   Politics.
   Science and technology.
   Social change and improvement.
   Personal change and improvement.

10. Anything else about him.

WHAT MAN CAN MAKE
OF MAN
Karl H. Hertz

Genetic programming could put an end to the
biological diversity that has done so much to
enrich man's life.

Genealogists of thought, unless they are extreme purists, must consider biologists and sociologists kinsmen of some sort, perhaps even kissing cousins. For a fairly recent ancestor common to them all is Charles Darwin, and behind him loom the figures of Thomas Malthus and Adam Smith. Herbert Spencer, who found in evolutionary theory an all-encompassing formula to explicate principles for all forms of life, individual and collective, served as the intellectual progenitor of several lineages of sociologists, from William Graham Sumner, that passionate iconoclast and nay-sayer, to the optimistic Reform Darwinist Lester F. Ward, apostle of progressive social development.

More instructive for our purposes than the use of biological concepts for sociological theory-building, however, are the social policies derived from biological teachings and the appeal to "science" for the legitimation of far-reaching political decisions. Evolutionary theory and early Galtonian doctrines of heredity furnished the bases for the eugenics movement and racialist theories and, specifically, for the development of the immigrant exclusion policies of the United States.

My paramount concern is not to chide the biologists for the uses made of rather primitive knowledge; nor am I interested in doing penance for the sins of the early sociologists. What is important as regards early hereditary theory is the attempt to institutionalize these findings of science into a set of social practices, most obviously in the sterilization laws of a number of states, less obviously in the ways, often diverse, in which some of these findings have been handled in the political arena. Here we have a primitive paradigm of how science becomes incorporated into social practice.

WHO WILL GUARD THE GUARDIANS?

Today's advances in biology—specifically the growing understanding of the genetic code and the increasing skill in synthesizing life, to mention only two areas of rapidly accelerating knowledge—raise issues of population control fraught with consequences far more revolutionary than either the earlier interventions of the eugenists or the exclusions of the ethnocentrists. In the light of these revolutionary possibilities we must ask the biologists not only what man can make of man but also who shall be the trustee of these powers. And who will guard the guardians?

Scientists, for good reasons, prefer to view their discipline from within. Their primary interest lies in safeguarding freedom of research and the disciplined elaboration of ideas. For most of them the world of science is autonomous, ascetically dedicated to truth, governed by impersonal and universal norms according to which ideas are screened and new discoveries elaborated. The administration and public use of the findings of science are not normally part of that world.

But science can no longer avoid the issues connected with the translation of its findings into social practice. The question is not the employment of science in the construction of world views, nor is it the forays made by philosophers and liberal clergymen to appropriate scientific categories for their own use: these, scientists can disavow and ignore. But there is a form of institutionalizing science whose existence depends on science. The very nature of the institutionalization, the translation of scientific knowledge into social practice, carries normative consequences.

SCIENCE AS SOCIETY'S SERVANT

No science can really escape being a servant of society. Each science as it has developed has provided the basis for one or more technologies—bridges from "pure science" to the everyday affairs of men. Some of these technologies have had far-reaching consequences for the daily routines of human life. Medicine offers an immediate example of application of biological knowledge. The use of ecology in conservation is an equally important if less obvious example. Early eugenics was a primitive effort in the same direction, an effort which largely failed.

Scientists may disavow as foreign to science the values to which many of the eugenists appealed. But this disclaimer does not dispose of the issue, for at the moment when a scientist or any other person perceives that a given scientific discovery has a human application, certain inescapable questions arise: on whom and under what conditions shall this discovery be used, and to what kinds of social goals should it be instrumental. Scientists themselves rarely preside over the application of their findings. Rather, it is persons scientifically trained to some degree, sometimes minimal, who act as the executors of science in its social application, with or without the help of lay boards, office clerks, and others whose knowledge and insight may be quite limited. That is, our problem is not one of science but of the technologies derived from it.

Technologies may be viewed as ways in which science is "socialized." Alongside the community of pure scientists, often intermingled with it, there grows up a community of professional practitioners which, like all communities, develops its codes of ethics. These codes differ from the codes of "pure science" at one important point. For while the latter codes quite properly center on the protection of objectivity, the focal point of professional codes is "right conduct," i.e., maintaining the integrity of professional practice. They offer guidelines for the use of knowledge.

The ethic that develops—this point must be underscored—is not derived from the scientific findings. When we consider social policy, we must recognize that scientists may in their prescription of what is "good" for man be expressing the prejudices of their upbringing or their commitment to a Platonic political ideology in which they are the philosopher-kings who can shape the future. In raising questions about the competence of biologists to determine the optimal genotype, I am not impugning their scientific knowledge; I am pointing out that when one moves from knowledge to practice, one inevitably becomes entangled in questions that are not really scientific. That is, to prescribe the genetic constitution of the man of the future, to bring him into being via sperm banks and genetic surgery, is to claim to know what the ideal human being ought to be like. This is not biology but ethics and moral philosophy.

In one sense ethics is inescapable when a science is "socialized" into a technology. We can and must always ask: What legitimates the moral concerns of the biotechnician, the fellow who will carry out these programs? Where do—and where shall—his values come from? Similarly, we must ask what justifies turning the application of genetics to improve the species in ways which do not interfere with human freedom into an imperialistic program that would presumably eliminate all but a few human genotypes. Even granting that this would be an evolutionary advantage—a question that must remain open—who is so wise that he can make the choice?

The possibilities of remaking what evolution has thus far brought into being go far beyond the improvement of the human species; they include the reshaping of the human environment. But this is a different question from the one on which I wish to concentrate. The issue is most urgent with respect to man. Technologically much of what Professor H. J. Muller suggests—notably in his *Studies in Genetics* (Indiana University Press, 1962)—is already practicable or will very soon be so. Hence, we must raise not only the question of policy but also the political question: how shall the execution of this program be organized?

Without laboring the point—leaving out all sorts of questions—we must ask, for example, who shall decide whose sperm is to be deposited in the sperm bank? Or, later on, whose ova shall be chosen? As a practicing politician, I know that research scientists and Nobel prize winners rarely sit on local boards of public affairs. These positions fall to the comparatively less informed, to people not always uncorruptible and unprejudiced; and, in addition, the daily routine is usually in the hands of clerk-typists and secretaries. If Thomas Jefferson was right when he said in his letter to John Adams that Whig and Tory are terms belonging to natural history, shall we also exclude Goldwater Republicans—and, in the age of the great consensus, perhaps Kennedy Democrats—from being depositors in the First National Sperm Bank of Bloomington, Indiana? Do we really want to run the political risks of programming human heredity?

THRESHOLD OF A REVOLUTION

In this connection we may well ask two questions: The first, put quite cold-bloodedly, is: Can we avoid it? The late John von Neumann once said that whatever is technologically possible will be done. Genetic programming is a distinct possibility, not nearly as remote as laymen would like to believe.

130

Granted that we undertake this programming: what then of the evolutionary effects—first, the effects with respect to man; second, the effects with respect to the social order?

In another context J. Bronowski has asked: "What truths can be stable in the soul of man, so easily mutilated, by nature so changeable?" If the millenniums from Neanderthal days to the present have worked changes in man; if indeed, as sociologists teach, the character of man is covariant with his social and cultural milieu, then these changes have generally come with glacier-like slowness. They have represented evolutionary selection and adaptation without the self-conscious direction of man.

Today the situation has changed drastically. We may be standing on the threshold of a major revolution in human history, biological and social. Turning the clock back has never been a successful response to a revolution. We must instead turn to other questions.

For the most part the development of codes of professional ethics has been a "natural" process of growth, as unconscious as the evolutionary process itself. Indeed, as historians of science know, Darwinian biology and Manchester economics shared common viewpoints as to the immutable autonomy of the processes of nature. Laissez-faire seemed of necessity the proper rule for both realms, since man's powers of intervention not only were meager but their employment was fundamentally imprudent. To "let nature take its course" was to guarantee the best outcome. Often calling upon evolutionary theory for legitimation, a whole school of political economists made laissez-faire its battle cry.

Today we cannot entrust the development of new codes of professional ethics to the vagaries of random cultural developments. Doubly so, because in earlier times the Western nations, where technologies flourished, possessed a high degree of consensus on many matters of human conduct. But "moral philosophy" has become rudderless, and our century is marked by cultural heterogeneity. Under these conditions, what results from the chance cross-fertilization of science and culture may be destructive, if not lethal, in its consequences.

A 'BRAVE NEW WORLD'?

Can we successfully institutionalize the process of biotechnical change? Or perhaps—since we know that there will be some kind of institutionalization—we should ask: What kinds of values will be dominant in the professional codes of the biotechnicians? Never before has the pressure of technological change pushed so hard against the norm-generating capacity of a social order. "Genetic programming" may be a development of the same historic proportions as atomic energy. We are now faced with programs of implementation. Some of the programmers even seem to know what the genetic constitution of the "ideal man" of the future should be. But do they, do we really know? By what criteria is this ideal man to be determined? Must not religious, ethical, and political considerations weigh as heavily as biological ones in our reflections as to whether we ought to take this step? Coping with these questions may require among biologists a breakthrough as radical as the one which led to establishment of the *Bulletin of the Atomic Scientists*. Let me draw upon medicine for an analogy. Central to medical ethics, especially in the borderline instance of euthanasia, has been respect for the patient as a person. Norms requiring consent for surgical procedure, etc., indicate that, with whatever shortcomings, medicine at its best does not manipulate human organisms as things.

Moreover, "genetic programming" is not the only possibility. We must also accept the fact that life can be brought into being in the laboratory. At present all these developments are, of course, still extremely primitive. But can we rule out the "brave new world" in which "man" can come into being in an "artificial womb"?

In short, is man really ready to play God? This is not just the general question whether man ought to have the right to manipulate his own biological constitution. What is crucial is that one set of men, the biotechnicians, will be intervening in the lives of other people, determining the traits of other people's children, present "parents" with children not of their own "procreation." The objects of this programming—in whatever form it is carried out—may easily turn out to be the poor and the powerless, presumably of "inferior" stock. For any application of this knowledge will take place within the framework of the existing distributions of power and privilege. Specifically, my question is not primarily whether genetic programming and other developments will come, but under what conditions and limitations, with what protection of human rights and prudent constraint of utopianism. How shall limits and directions be set? Even: How does the creature-become-creator understand himself, his powers, and his responsibilities?

These are not science-fiction issues. We must ask in all seriousness: What can man make of man? Where shall the normative decisions lie? What about the consequences for what we know as the human family? Who shall frame the code of ethics for the biotechnicians? Who is competent to define the "ideal man"?

Recent philosophical discussions among scientists—e.g., Michael Polanyi and, in this context, John Platt—stress the degree to which man, that rather defective species we know and are, shapes the world through his knowing and doing. These discussions may foreshadow a new understanding of man as person, as participant in the process of discovery. At the same time, they imply a rejection of many of the behavioristic and mechanistic concepts of man that are now taken for granted.

DEFENDING AGAINST DEHUMANIZATION

Still we ask: Who is man? Which conception of man will determine how and when we apply the biotechnical skills we are developing? This is not an obscurantist argument against technology. It is a question of how policy shall be made under conditions of knowledge constantly subject to revision and correction.

What can man make of man? Does the answer not finally rest on the understanding of man which develops within a technical community? It is a fact that preoccupation with the "objective accounts" of human illness and with the physiology and chemistry of the human organism often predisposes doctors of medicine to see man in less than personal terms. The professional requirements of "objectivity" and "impersonality"—norms that are indispensable—tend to transform the patient into a complicated piece of malfunctioning machinery. Perhaps the conservatism inherent in the Hippocratic oath has been one of our defenses against the dehumanization of medicine.

But as we cross new frontiers we leave behind the traditions that informed our thinking. A great deal may depend on where the weights fall. René Dubos and other biologists insist that we must attend to the ways in which man differs from his near relatives, not just to the ways in which he is like them; for it is in the differences that the uniqueness of man is found. The biotechnician would set up one kind of program if he shared this view, another if he held anti-Dubos ideas.

MORAL NEUTRALITY: HAZARDOUS LUXURY

If the technician also takes seriously the insights into human behavior contributed by some branches of the behavioral sciences—insights as to the depths of personality and the role of the symbolic and the unconscious—then the professional code developed may be quite different from the code based on doctrines of mechanism and behaviorism. Above all, if the biotechnician, along with the behavioral scientist, accepts the proposition that we are still far from understanding man, the development of biotechnics will surely take another tack. To begin programming on the assumption that all the evidence is in could have tragic consequences. Nor may we be able to undo the consequences. To be sure, our immigration laws have been amended—but it hasn't been easy.

What will man make of man? One of the glories of our species—despite all the heartache attendant on living—has been the diversity within it. This diversity—both of genetic endowment and of cultural development—has contributed much to man's spread over the planet and, I would argue, to the richness of life in every society. Biological diversity is a kind of counterpart of political pluralism. But will not the biotechnicians be tempted to shape us according to a few patterns they prefer? All questions of norms aside, what will this limited patterning do to man's capacity to survive as a biological organism?

As a sociologist, I also have what I consider a legitimate question which arises from a professional preoccupation. Will not "genetic programming" lead us again to overemphasize the role of heredity in human development? Do we not face a serious problem in personality theory at this point? Is there not a tendency among some geneticists to treat the question of personality development as almost exclusively a biological given?

It seems to me that the biologist cannot much longer afford the luxury of "moral neutrality." In Darwinism's heyday biologists, philosophers, and popularizers alike seized upon evolution as the basis for a new ethic. I would not be so brazen as to recommend a repetition of this undertaking. But I would suggest that in an open universe, where the evolutionary process is one agent of change, we must—now that we have reached the point of self-conscious direction of the process—ask ethical questions of a kind that cannot be answered without the counsel of the biologists, indeed of the best of them. The nuclear physicists could not turn over the application of atomic power to the engineers; no more will the biologists be able to turn their new knowledge over to the biotechnicians.

If what is unique about man is his "personhood"—man as a self-conscious center of action—must we not incorporate this as a constant into our biotechnology? And how?

It may very well be true—I believe it is—that the content of science, any science, does not in and of itself validate an ethic. In this sense it is quite obvious that our works do not save us. The basic moral affirmations needed to shape the ethical codes for the employment of our biological knowledge will need a different kind of validation. Here the affirmations of faith must count; and the kinds of communities of faith men belong to may be decisive.

Perhaps even this question thus becomes inescapable for the biologist as he ponders what man can make of man.

TRY THESE PROJECTS FOR—
WHAT MAN CAN MAKE OF MAN,
by Hertz

---

1. *A code of ethics for scientists.*

According to Jewish tradition, God gave Moses 613 commandments in the Bible which, later, leaders tried to reduce to the smallest possible number of requirements for the "ideal" Jew.

Look up each of the following, and list these requirements in each case:

Eleven requirements, by David, in Psalm 15.

Ten, in the Ten Commandments, in Exodus 20.

Three, by Micah, in 6:8.

One, by Isaiah, in 56:1.

One, by Amos, in 5:4.

One, by Habbakuk, in 2:4.

One, by Hillel, based on Leviticus 19:18.

Compile a list of ethical requirements for scientists from *Science and Human Values*, by J. Bronowski, and compare the two lists. Draw up a code of Ethics for Scientists based on your two lists, plus other ideas of your own.

2. *Construct the "ideal" man, in two steps.*

■ Set up a suggestion box in which classmates drop ideas about his mental, physical, emotional, religious, moral, and ethical traits. (Be sure to specify whether you want these suggestions to be serious or satirical or both.)

■ Make a life-size poster of a human figure incorporating *all* the suggestions you receive.

3. *Express yourself.*

■ Write an editorial: "I'm Satisfied the Way I Am."

■ Draw up an amendment to the Constitution forbidding (or permitting or limiting) biogenetic experimentation.

■ "I Believe"—your personal credo about man's future, expressing your faith that wisdom will triumph over stupidity.

4. *Go creative.*

It's a century or two from now, and biogenetic man is a reality.

■ For a demonstration against "Planned Personality," make a list of demands of the "Board of Human Control."

■ Devise questions and answers for an interview with the last human being allowed to be born and grow naturally in a world of created people.

■ Write an historical sketch of changes in religion (especially Judaism), education, sex, marriage, family, work, play.

■ Report the news of an archeological "find"—the prayer for guidance of the scientist who discovered the final step in the process of creating and controlling human life.

5. *Research.*

■ Eugenics—producing better human beings through control of hereditary factors.

The history and progress of this science/technology.

The concepts of Plato, the ancient Greek philosopher, in his *Republic,* Chapter 16, as compared with those of a modern expert, Jacques Ellul, in his *The Technological Society.*

The distorted applications of eugenics in the racialist theories of Nazi Germany or the immigration policies of the United States in the twentieth century.

■ Euthenics—shaping the human environment, developing human well-being by improving living conditions.

■ Biogenetics—creation and control of human characteristics by chemical and physical techniques for manipulating the genes. Look into memory transfer, medicated survival, suspended animation.

■ Current opinion, pro and con, on heredity, environment, eugenics, euthenics, biogenetics, etc.—of both physical and social scientists, but especially of religious thinkers, and even more especially of Jewish thinkers. (Consult the *Reader's Guide to Periodical Literature* and the *New York Times Index* for the very latest articles and news reports.)

■ Technology the destroyer—look up the legends and stories about Frankenstein, and look into the modern term robot.

Summarize legends in Jewish tradition about the creation of human life and their ethical implications, particularly the "golem" stories. (Resources: *Jewish Encyclopedia,* VI, 36–37; N. Ausubel, *A Treasury of Jewish Folklore,* 603–612.)

Are these stories prophetic warnings of what may happen to mankind? Use evidence and examples to show that these warnings are likely or unlikely to come true.

After You Have Read—
WHAT MAN CAN MAKE OF MAN,
by Hertz

Discuss these questions:

1. What are the points of agreement and disagreement between Hertz, Weinberg, and Ferry? For example, according to Hertz," . . . our problem is not one of science but of the technologies derived from it." Do you agree?

    Or has he overlooked still another kind of problem? A quick review of the two preceding essays may give you some answers.

2. Is the following statement valid? Why or why not?

    "The creation or control of human life would have to be based on certain criteria, since there would be a wide range of choice as to just what kind of human beings to create or develop. Such criteria imply that there is a superior form of human being, that one kind of person is better than another. Science and technology will soon have the power to produce one kind of person rather than another, but science and technology by themselves can never decide what makes one kind of person better than another. For this decision, science and technology must turn to religion, morals, ethics, and the other spiritual traditions of mankind."

3. Which Jewish values below would be threatened by biogenetic programming of human beings?

    The uniqueness of each person.
    Man is created *"betzelem Elohim,"* in the image of God.
    The primary reason for sexual intercourse is procreation.
    Belief in the existence of a "soul."

4. Think of a concrete example to prove or disprove each of the following statements by Hertz:

    "Science becomes incorporated into social practice."

    "No science can really escape being a servant of society."

    "Our problem is not one of science but of the technologies derived from it."

    "Scientists may in their prescription of what is 'good' for man be expressing the prejudices of their upbringing."

    "When one moves from knowledge to practice, one inevitably becomes entangled in questions that are not really scientific."

    "The character of man is covariant with his social and cultural milieu."

137

"We may be standing on the threshold of a major revolution in human history, biological and social."

"What results from the chance cross-fertilization of science and culture may be destructive, if not lethal, in its consequences."

"Man shapes the world through his knowing and doing."

"Preoccupation with the 'objective accounts' of human illness and with the physiology and chemistry of the human organism often predispose doctors of medicine to see man in less than personal terms."

"It is in the differences between man and his near relatives that the uniqueness of man is found."

"One of the glories of our species has been the diversity within it."

"The biologist cannot much longer afford the luxury of 'moral neutrality.'"

5. When scientists are able to fashion human beings, who should decide what kind of people they should make?
   Give reasons for your choices.
   Biotechnicians—those who know how to do it.
   Scientists in general.
   The government.
   Philosophers.
   Religious leaders.
   _____ (Your own suggestions.)
   A combination of _____

6. Read the news item below reprinted from the *New York Times,* January 6, 1969. What changes in our attitudes to science and religion are likely to take place when all this comes true? What do you think will happen to Judaism?

   "By tinkering with the fundamental molecular events associated with heredity and development, geneticists hold out the prospect of correcting almost any unwanted human condition—cancer, birth defects, diabetes, hemophilia, aging. They speak of imparting superior intelligence to all, of preserving desirable traits perpetually, of turning the chemical units of heredity, called genes, on and off at will . . . . The concept of genetic engineering, until recently a dream of such visionaries as the late Nobel laureate Herman J. Muller, is so close to reality that some scientists have suggested a moratorium on research to give society time to figure out where the development is leading."

   According to geneticists quoted in this account, within a generation or two we will be able to preselect our children's sex, regenerate defective or damaged organs, preserve sperm and egg cells of superior individuals long after death and use them to create new human beings, live 90 or 100 years with full vigor, change sex at will, and perform other "miracles."

7. Here are two views of religion in the twenty-first century. Which is right? Have you a prediction of your own? What must be done to ensure a relevant Judaism a generation from now?

"By the twenty-first century, religious believers are likely to be found only in small sects, huddled together to resist a worldwide secular culture . . . in a surprise-free world. I see no reversal of the process of secularization . . . I think people will become so bored with what religious groups have to offer that they will look elsewhere . . . ." (Peter L. Burger, leading Lutheran layman in the *New York Times,* January 25, 1968.)

"The nervous scurrying for relevance by politically active clergymen may represent the sickness not the health of American religion . . . A large part of what passes for liberal religion in America is a rewriting of *The Nation* and *The New Republic.* That is not the job of religion. What people come to religion for is an ultimate metaphysical hunger and when this hunger is not satisfied, religion declines . . . Liberal religion is faintly out of date. We are moving past the social questions of ultimate concern." (Rabbi Arthur Hertzberg in the *New York Times,* March, 1968.)

8. Go back to your ideal human being in the "Before You Read" section for this essay. Which of your prescriptions for such a human being seems to be based on *Jewish* values? You may wish to compare your list with Psalms 1 and 15, for example.

ASK YOURSELF AGAIN

After you've finished Part II, "Technology and Religious Values," go back over all the "Before You Read" questions so far, including those for Part I. Reconsider your answers, and write out as many questions, statements, answers, or ideas as you like, under these headings:

1. I've changed my mind about—

2. I still feel the same way I did before about—

3. I feel more certain than before about—

4. I feel less certain than before about—

See suggestions in "Ask Yourself Again" Part I, page 86.

Part III

SCIENCE AND ETHICS

ETHICS
OF
THE
SCIENTIFIC
AGE,
by Heitler

Give a specific example for each item.

If you can't, skip it for now.

1. An ethical value that has remained roughly the same as it was 2000 or 3000 years ago.

2. A recent change, in man's physical environment or in man himself, that calls for new ethical principles.

3. Interference with personal freedom today.

4. Mass propaganda aimed at depriving individuals of their independent judgment and driving them instead into the direction desired by others.

5. An invention of questionable ethical value.

6. A rule needed for good functioning of society or government, in contrast with a basic moral or ethical principle.

7. A cultural achievement of mankind due to an individual person, rather than to a large group.

8. A life process that cannot be understood on the basis of physics and chemistry alone.

9. A life process in man that is not identical to those in animals.

10. An effect of chemical or physical interference with life processes that become apparent only many years later.

11. A biological application of a scientific discovery that rests on partial knowledge.

12. Proof that a true and complete knowledge of life processes does not yet exist.

For the examples you thought of, to judge whether they are good or bad, would you call on science or religion? Both? Neither?

ETHICS OF THE
SCIENTIFIC AGE
W. Heitler

Do new technological developments neces-
sitate a new ethic for contemporary man?

T HE DEVELOPMENTS in natural science, which started about 300 years ago and became particularly fast in this century, have made human actions possible which were previously unthinkable. It has often been said that our ethical development has not kept pace with this technological progress, that our ethical values remain roughly the same as they were 2000 or 3000 years ago.

Are these ethical values still sufficient in view of the vastly increased capacities for action by individuals, groups, and governments? Is ethics independent of the mental makeup of the people for whom it is supposed to be valid? New factors may arise in the development of mankind, which call for a new ethical orientation—changes in man's physical environment (caused by new technology, by the replacement of natural, by artificial conditions of life, etc.) or more profound changes in man himself. Such changes may make parts of the existing moral laws meaningless, or may demand altogether new laws. Profound changes in mental makeup also may occur, such as the rise of what we now call the "scientific attitude" (replacing the "religious attitude" of past centuries) or the increased value which we now assign to the freedom of the individual.

We will select a few recent technical inventions, and examine them from the ethical point of view.

THE DIRECTED MULTITUDE

Chemistry has given us drugs permitting the alteration of man's mental and emotional makeup. There are drugs which remove inhibition and fear; they enable an individual to perform deeds which he would normally not dare to perform because of concern with his own safety. There are other drugs which paralyze the will power and make men follow the suggestions of others. Admittedly, these are rather crude interferences with the inner life of individuals. In a more subtle manner, but to a vastly greater extent, modern advertising interferes with this life. The things praised by advertising, be they products of industry, opinions on certain matters, or election candidates, are not offered in a way permitting everyone to form his own opinion. Instead, advertising works through the semiconscious or subconscious mind. This way of gaining influence on people has been much studied psychologically. An extreme case is the recently invented "subliminal" suggestion: a slogan is projected on the screen by means of very short light flashes—too short to be perceived consciously. Yet, the perception works on the subconscious mind and leads to an unarticulated desire, which later rises to the surface of consciousness. This is an obvious interference with the freedom of the individual.

Recent neurological research has succeeded in localizing the material seat of certain emotions—pleasure, pain, thirst, etc., in the brain. It thus opened the possibility of influencing these emotions by physical means. Experiments have shown that it is possible, through radiation or other agents, to create or destroy

144

such emotions in animals. It is probably only a matter of time until applications to human beings will become possible. In this way, the emotional life of man could be artificially changed. We don't wish to argue whether it would be justifiable to free a person in this way from a toothache, but it is certain that possibilities arise here of influencing the inner life of the individual, and that the far-reaching consequences of such interference can hardly be foreseen now.

In all these examples—and there are many others—we are dealing with interference, often without the explicit agreement of the person concerned, with the inner sphere of his personality and, above all, with his personal freedom. How are these inventions to be evaluated ethically? Anyone for whom personal freedom is a positive value is bound to regard such interference with suspicion and refuse it as immoral.

We are confronted, however, with a peculiar situation. There is hardly a concept more frequently mentioned by public speakers or in print than the concept of "freedom." We are very proud of having acquired freedom. But personal freedom is not included in the now generally accepted moral code. Freedom of speech and freedom of the press are guaranteed by the constitutions of many nations; it is a punishable offense to deprive a person of the freedom of movement; yet, more subtle encroachments upon the integrity of one's personality are not regarded as morally objectionable. On the contrary, freedom of the press and of speech, assisted by radio and television, often means freedom to engage in mass propaganda aimed at depriving individuals of their independent judgment and driving them instead into the direction desired by others. This is the antithesis of freedom. It converts free men into a directed multitude. Such misuse of technological inventions would not be possible if protection of free personality were part of our moral code, as is the protection of our physical existence. Whence this confusion? A few reasons can be given without claim to complete clarification.

INDIVIDUAL FREEDOM

The high value which we attach today to the freedom of the individual is a comparatively recent development, dating back approximately to the Renaissance. In the earlier times, certain individuals could develop in freedom, but there was seldom talk of such freedom having to be granted to all, as a matter of principle. It required the Reformation and a series of revolutions in various countries to establish this principle. But our more than 2000 year old ethics did not adjust itself to it. In ethics, personal freedom has not yet taken deep root.

The new threats to individual freedom derive more or less directly from technical achievements, such as radio, television, and instant communications. Without them these threats would not be possible, at least not to the present extent. Science has won through its successes an enormous prestige. New inventions are put to practical use without question, because they are "scientific."

145

Everything is permitted if it serves science—truly or presumptively. Rarely is the question of the ethical value of an invention raised. So it came about that the major threats to individualism and freedom, made possible by the new technology, have met with very little resistance.

In the past, ethics was closely connected with religion. Simultaneously with the development of science, traditional religion became gradually devalued, and nothing that could give a basis for ethical values has taken its place. For want of a new ethical orientation, we stuck to the inherited moral code, which, deprived of its religious base, became more and more formalized. Some historians interpreted it merely as a set of rules needed for good functioning of a social organism, or for effective government; any deeper association of the ethical code with the human being was gradually lost.

Today, we have no ethical directives which would correspond to the new situation of mankind, no generally accepted principles which would protect the freedom of the individual, nor any that would as much as put a positive value on this freedom. One may argue that it is not so certain that individualism must be preferred to mass uniformity. In recent times, it has often seemed as if uniformity corresponded to a deep-seated desire in many people—perhaps because of their fear of freedom and the responsibility that goes with it. And yet, nobody openly denies that freedom is a desirable ideal. Even notorious suppressors of freedom never dared to say what they wanted was unfreedom; instead, they merely twisted the meaning of the word freedom. Freedom seems to be something that answers a deep longing in the innermost being of man.

The term freedom only makes sense when applied to an individual, never to a mass of people. The highest cultural achievements of mankind have been due to individuals, at least in modern times. Even proper reception of such cultural achievements requires a certain individualization. Many now would deem impossible the creation of true cultural achievements by mankind transformed into a uniform mass. We believe that a development toward greater individualism is desirable; but we do not possess, even in outline, general ethical principles which would support this development. The consequence is a cultural and ethical chaos, in which practically everything that science and technology offer is considered permissible and even desirable.

PHYSICOCHEMICAL MAN

Let us now consider another class of scientific applications, whose purpose is purely biological. We do not want to minimize the success of many modern pharmaceutical products. Nevertheless, grave dangers become apparent in this field, due to lack of proper biological thinking—dangers which raise serious ethical problems.

A large part of modern pharmacology is based on the following scientific theory: in the living organism, complicated physical and chemical processes take place, and they can be influenced by physical-chemical agents from the outside. It is assumed—consciously or subconsciously—that these processes represent the *whole* of the life process, that life is nothing but a particularly complicated physicochemical system. Also, it is assumed that these chemical and physical processes are analogous in man and in the higher animals—an assumption also supported by Darwin's theory of evolution.

This is a half-truth. The most typical life processes cannot be understood on the basis of physics and chemistry alone. This is also the opinion of some biologists, but not of all. Life processes in higher animals and in man are intimately interwoven with mental processes. In man, the latter are, of course, completely different from those in even the highest animals. Therefore, one must expect that at least some biological functions will be quite different in man and in animals. The recent thalidomide tragedy is an illustration. Animal experiments had shown this drug to be harmless; the same experiments had shown that it is inactive in animals as a sleeping drug—in contrast to the effect it produces in man. The only correct conclusion would have been that nothing whatsoever could be concluded from animal experiments about the effects of the drug on man—and fortunately, this conclusion had been drawn in some countries (for example, in the U.S. and in Switzerland). This, and similar examples, casts doubt on the thesis of biological similarity of man and animal, which has been often accepted and is still often accepted almost dogmatically.

The development of psychosomatic medicine in recent years has clearly illustrated the intimate connection between the psychic and the somatic (physical-chemical) processes in man. Thus, life processes in man are neither purely physical-chemical, nor are they identical to those in animals.

The thalidomide case is a particulary drastic example of almost immediate damaging consequences of the use of a drug. In some cases, the damaging effects of chemical or physical interference with life processes become apparent only many years later. A well-known example is radiation damage, which often becomes obvious only 10 or 15 years after irradiation. The maximum permissible dose for x-ray irradiation has been repeatedly reduced in recent years, because of such observations. Similarly, the effects of carcinogenic chemicals, applied in small doses over long periods, may become apparent only after many years.

Today, we are confronted with wide application of chemical and physical agents, the long-range consequences of which cannot be foreseen. It may be, for example, that some widely used insecticides have unforseeable long-range effects, even if they do not have the more immediate harmful effects described by Rachel Carson in *Silent Spring*. The happy-go-lucky biological application of chemical and physical discoveries (which constitute a major part of applied science) rests on an unwarranted acceptance of the materialistic interpretation of life. A partial science is put in place of the whole. We simply do not possess a complete knowledge of biological processes, comparable to our mastery of the physical processes in inorganic matter afforded by physics and chemistry. As we have seen, at least part of the applications of this partial science turned out to be inimical to life, in a manner that could not be foreseen solely with the aid of scientific thinking as used in physics and chemistry.

We must regard biological applications which rest on partial knowledge of life as irresponsible. Of course, scientists who practice these applications are not aware of acting irresponsibly. On the contrary, they work with a maximum of conscientiousness possible within the framework of their partial science. However, scientific applications which have even a chance of inflicting general damage on life in the future cannot be justified from the ethical point of view.

The root of this irresponsibility lies in the fact that *the part is taken for the whole*. We suggest that the thesis on which this irresponsibility is based—namely, that life is nothing but a complicated case of physics and chemistry—is itself immoral.

The lack of appreciation of the limits of present scientific knowledge of life has direct and very dangerous consequences for the position of man in our world picture. It leads to identification of man with a complicated physicochemical mechanism, and this, in turn, to devaluation of all that is genuinely human. A mechanism is amoral; "mechanization" of life, be it conscious or unconscious, is bound to lead to destruction of all ethics. If we consider life in general and the freedom of the individual in particular as positive values, we are forced to consider the mechanistic-materialistic concept of life as immoral.

A NEW SCIENTIFIC ETHIC

Let us return to our original subject. It should now be clear that we need nothing more urgently than a new ethics, adapted to the present scientific possibilities of human action. It will not be easy to develop it. We cannot imagine a scientist, philosopher, lawyer, or theologian sitting down at his desk and composing a new moral code. Rather, the creation of a new ethics must be a development comparable to a great scientific discovery, or to the creation of a masterpiece of art. That moral creation *is* possible is shown by the example of Albert Schweitzer and his thesis of "respect for all life." On the other hand, we cannot afford to do nothing and wait for this creation. A few points can be outlined even now:

In the first place, a main requirement is to recognize that the main body of present scientific activity concerns only one aspect of nature—the material—and cannot be regarded as providing a full grasp of reality. As we have seen, this *totum pro parte* is at the root of the present ethical chaos. The purpose of this article was to awaken the consciousness of scientists to this limitation. The next step should not be too difficult. There are enough people, including some scientists, who possess a highly developed conscience. As soon as it has become common knowledge that, for example, a true and complete knowledge of life processes

148

does not yet exist, this conscience will direct research into more healthy directions (in the literal as well as in the figurative sense). One chief point of new scientific ethics will have to be respect for life, which is not yet explored, and respect for free human personality. It is to be hoped that in the course of time, new lines of scientific ethics will develop; without them, mankind will stumble from catastrophe to catastrophe.

Try These Projects For—
ETHICS OF THE SCIENTIFIC AGE,
by Heitler

---

1. *Know yourself.*

   Draw up a list of your own values—anything you consider so important to get and keep that you would sacrifice almost anything else in order to do so. Make the list as long as possible. Then cross off (a) anything that is a temporary value which probably won't be a value to you in the future, and (b) anything very personal to you and probably not a value to anyone else. Now cross off anything that is not in some way a *Jewish* value—only Jews have it, or Jews have it more than non-Jews, or Jews have a different feeling about it from non-Jews. What's left, if anything, are your own personal Jewish values.

   Compile a class list of the Jewish values left on all individual lists, and compare with the Jewish values given in *Jewish Values*, by Louis Jacobs; *The Future of the American Jew*, by Mordecai M. Kaplan, pp. 246–339; and "Guiding Principles of Reform Judaism."

   What conclusions do you draw from the comparison?

2. *Express yourself.*

   ■ Act out this (imaginary) scene at the home of a rabbi—One of his members comes to see him with a problem. The advertising firm he works for is going to try subliminal advertising—flashing a selling message on a tv or movie screen so fast you can't notice it, but so often that gradually it builds up a subconscious desire to buy the advertised brand or product. He is to be put in charge of the project, with a big promotion and salary raise. Should he do it? If he won't, they'll simply get someone else. On the other hand, is it immoral, unethical? You can include the rabbi's wife and the man's wife in the scene if you want to, and maybe even have the rabbi phone the president of the advertising company to come on over and join the discussion. One tip, however—Before you tackle this little sociodrama, better ask your rabbi how he actually might handle such a problem, to guide your actor-rabbi to be as realistic as possible.

   ■ Draw up a formal citation of honor to be presented to an inventor. (He can be living or dead; the invention can be real or imaginary; you can be serious or satirical.)

   ■ Draw up a Code of Ethics for scientists and inventors—What they must do, may do, and must not do about discoveries and inventions that are potentially immoral or unethical. (For example: Should a scientist accept a government grant to develop a new technique for warfare? For controlling man's minds? For propaganda?)

3. *Be creative.*

■ Design the cover for a book on science (or technology) and religion (or human values). Clarify your own thinking first. Do you see two sharply separated parts of a design? A clash of conflict? Cooperating partners? Estranged partners? One destroying the other? Or what?

■ Make a drawing, poster, cartoon, or design to illustrate Heitler's idea that scientists tend to think their partial knowledge of human life represents all there is to know about it—they take the part for the whole.

■ On a time line, show the technological "explosion" in some aspect of modern life, e.g., for travel—walking, horses, boats for centuries, then suddenly autos, planes, rocketships. If you agree with Heitler that we need a new ethics today, show the "old" ethics (Ten Commandments, etc.) as needing updating; if you disagree, show how our ethical imperatives have not changed.

■ A time line, showing on one side of the line the major developments in the history of science, and on the other the major developments in the history of religion. Be ready to explain any conclusions that you can draw from the result.

4. *Get action.*

■ Propose to the religious school board that the topic of science and religion be introduced earlier in the religious school curriculum—in a very elementary way in lower grades, but the middle grades can deal with some of the same problems you're coming up against in this course. You'll find some good suggestions in "Enriching Our Curriculum with Science," by Toby K. Kurzband and David Kraus, in *The Jewish Teacher*, UAHC, for March, 1949.

You might send the school board a letter, a formal resolution, or invite a representative to visit your class and discuss it with you.

Be sure you have your reasons well worked out to justify introducing science topics and problems to various grades. Try to have definite topics to suggest, and be able to show their relationship to *religious* education.

■ Draw up a set of specific questions you have about the ethics of science and technology, and ask your rabbi to answer them in a sermon or in a message in his congregational bulletin.

5. *Research.*

■ Drugs and the teenager—Who, why, what, how much, results, remedies. (Resources: Consult *Reader's Guide to Periodical Literature* and the *New York Times Index* for recent articles such as "LSD Spread in the U.S. Alarms Doctors and Police," the *New York Times*, February 23, 1967, Library Microfilm; Arthur H. Becker, "What the Minister Ought to Know about LSD," *Pastoral Psychology*,

Oct., 1965; "Pot and Parents," *Time,* August 30, 1968; Steven B. Jacobs, "Let's Stop Pushing the Marijuana Myth," *Dimensions in American Judaism,* Fall 1969.)

■ Subliminal advertising—Who, why, what, where, how, controls. (Resources: *Reader's Guide to Periodical Literature; New York Times Index;* Vance Packard, *The Hidden Persuaders.*)

■ Advertising techniques then and now—Analyze and compare persuasion techniques in the *New York Times* fifty to one hundred years ago (available in libraries on microfilm) and today, as to their interference with individual freedom, privacy, or personality development.

■ The thalidomide tragedy—What, when, where, why, how, results. (A new drug, considered "the perfect sleeping pill," produced over 12,000 deformed babies.)

AFTER YOU HAVE READ—
ETHICS OF THE SCIENTIFIC AGE,
by Heitler

Discuss these questions:

1. A "value" can be defined in two ways:

   Descriptive—whatever a person or group actually likes, prizes, esteems, desires, approves, or enjoys.

   Normative—whatever a person or group should like, prize, esteem, desire, approve, or enjoy.

   Heitler says our ethical values remain roughly the same as they were 2000 or 3000 years ago. For which definition of value is he right—descriptive, normative, both, neither? For which definition would his statement be right about *Jewish* values? Incidentally, are Jewish values descriptive or normative?

2. Heitler speaks of "the scientific attitude" today replacing "the religious attitude," without actually defining these attitudes. On the basis of his essay, how would he probably define them? Does one attitude repudiate the other, or can a person accept both attitudes?

3. Give some specific examples of individual freedom today in social customs, politics, personal life. Do we today, as Heitler claims, assign increased value to the freedom of the individual? Is our individual freedom today greater than it was in biblical or talmudic times? In the Middle Ages? A generation or two ago?

4. Fill in below, and compare the two:

   To me, "personal freedom" means_____

   To Heitler, "personal freedom" means_____

5. Work out your own or the class's distinctions between:

   Religion.

   Morality or morals.

   Ethics.

   Values.

   Does any of these terms include any of the others? Is any term just a synonym for all others? Do they all really represent different things? Test your answers out by trying to think of a religious act that would not be moral or ethical; an ethical act that would not be religious or a value; a value that would not be religious; and so on.

   Then (unless you're *too* confused by now) consider these two passages:

"Ethics is the vital principle of Judaism. Its religion aims to be, and is, moral doctrine. Love of God is knowledge of God, and that is knowledge of the ultimate moral purpose of mankind." (Hermaan Cohen.)

153

"Judaism is not merely ethical, but ethics constitutes its . . . essence." (Leo Baeck.)

Are morals, ethics, and values possible without religion? Are they possible without religion in Judaism?

6. Do we really need "a new ethics" today? Are there really "no ethical directives (corresponding) to the new situation of mankind" today? Or do certain basic values and ethics of Judaism still apply to the problems Heitler raises?

Consider God and man as copartners, reverence for life, responsibility of man for his fellow man, dignity of man, importance of the individual person.

7. Heitler attacks as immoral the prevalent modern idea that "practically everything that science and technology offer is considered permissible and even desirable." Many modern thinkers recognize and criticize the same trend in our thinking today—If you can do it, you have the right to do it, and should not be criticized or punished for doing it. Think of specific examples of things each of the following can do but in your opinion would not or should not do.

A big power (the U.S. or Russia).
A small power (Israel or South Vietnam).
The government (federal, state, local).
A business company.
A labor union.
A synagogue or church.
A parent.
You personally.
How many of your examples involve science or technology?

If few or none, weren't you guilty of Heitler's charge—scientific and technological accomplishments, because they are possible, didn't occur to you as being wrong? In any case, wherever your example is not scientific or technological, think of one that is. How hard or easy do you personally find it is to think of such examples of "can-do-but-shouldn't"? Is there a Jewish position on this problem?

8. Study the following passage, and then answer the questions. "If you study man by the method suited to chemistry, or even if you study him in the light of what you have learned about rats and dogs, it is certainly to be expected that what you discover will be what chemistry and animal behavior have to teach. But it is also not surprising or even significant if by such methods you fail to discover anything else." (Joseph Wood Krutch, *The Measure of Man.*)

Would Heitler agree or disagree? Quote him to prove your answer.

Would a scientific analysis of art, literature, or music be complete and final—or are there qualities in these experiences that are beyond any scientific analysis?

154

A computer can be designed to compose music, make a drawing, create a story. Does this fact answer the question above?

Do animals have a moral code? Know right from wrong? Sing and dance? Have a sense of humor? What sort of animal behavior is also true of man? What sort of human behavior is not true of animals? What sort of thing can you learn, and what sort of thing can you not learn, about one by studying the other?

9. Heitler calls immoral the idea that life is only a complex case of physical and chemical processes. What do you conclude about his religious belief? And why?

He is a theist, and believes in God. (If there is no God, no moral authority, transcending men and the universe, you can't call an idea "immoral"—only "proven," "disproven," or "unproven" according to scientific standards, or "pleasant," "unpleasant," or "neutral" according to personal standards. "Immoral" implies you are violating some basic, universal code of morality.)

He is an atheist, and does not believe in God. (Morality is just a group of laws or customs to protect its members or prevent conflict. Or else it's just a human characteristic like walking upright or having no tail, that just evolved naturally. You can call an idea "immoral" if it hurts people, or if people object to it—you don't need God to explain it, or justify it, or enforce it.)

He is an agnostic, and feels we just don't know everything about the world or about ourselves. (We only know a very small part of "the truth." That doesn't mean we'll never know more—but we have no right to think and act as if what we know is "the whole truth." We must recognize our ignorance, and be more careful about applying the little that we do know.)

10. According to Heitler, when we treat man as merely a complicated physico-chemical mechanism, we devaluate all that is "genuinely human." In between "mechanism" and "human," he seems to ignore plant and animal life. How would he—how would you, if you disagree with him—answer such questions as the following ones?

Are plants and animals only complicated physicochemical mechanisms, or do they too have "something else," and if so, what else?

Do animals have "something else," nonphysicochemical, beyond what plants have? What?

Do human beings have still something else again? What?

What does "genuinely human" mean exactly, specifically, with evidence or examples?

11. Go back to the "Before You Read" section for this essay, and see if now you can supply examples for any items you skipped before.

BEFORE YOU READ—

ETHICS
FOR
THE
SCIENTIST,
by Haybittle

Label each of the following values.

"A" means primary, basic, more important; "B" means secondary, less vital, less important.

_____ 1. Accuracy, truth to fact.

_____ 2. Freedom of thought and speech.

_____ 3. Tolerance, acceptance of dissent.

_____ 4. Justice, fair play.

_____ 5. Honor, human dignity.

_____ 6. Self-respect.

_____ 7. Tenderness, sensitivity to others' feelings.

_____ 8. Kindness, generosity.

_____ 9. Human intimacy, love.

_____10. Compassion, pity.

_____11. Concern for future generations.

_____12. Belief in a divine source of power in the universe.

Now go back and label each one again: "S" for a value you think is cultivated by the practice of science; "NS" for a value you think is not cultivated by the practice of science.

ETHICS FOR THE
SCIENTIST

John Haybittle

Scientists are discovering that what they do
and say has immense ethical significance.
Can the scientist still maintain the posture of
ethical neutrality in the face of the growing
importance of scientific achievement and its
impact on our lives?

METRIC 1

IN DISCUSSING the ethical responsibilities of scientists, I am concerned only with the responsibilities of the individual scientist for the consequences that result from his own scientific work. I am not concerned with the responsibilities of science as a branch of human activity or with the collective responsibilities of its practitioners as a social group. Ethics cannot be attributed to an abstraction such as science, and the ethics of scientists cannot be separated from the ethics of each individual scientist. When an attempt is made to distinguish between collective and individual responsibility, confusion always results. Dr. J. Bronowski, in "The Real Responsibilities of the Scientist" (December 1956 *Bulletin*), made just such an attempt, and some quotations from his article should clarify the point I am trying to make.

"In assessing collective responsibility," he writes, "we must explain to people that they are asking of scientists quite the wrong collective decision when they say 'you should not have invented this' or 'you should not have disclosed that.' This is asking us all to betray the public in the same way as Dr. Klaus Fuchs did, by asking scientists to make decisions which are for the nation to make. . . . Scientists have no right to betray the will of the nation."

He then goes on to discuss the responsibility of the individual scientist: "He is the keeper of his private conscience. He has the right to act individually as a conscientious objector. . . . He has a business to settle with his own conscience, the serious business whether he personally will engage in forms of research of which he does not morally approve."

These two statements seem to be irreconcilable when translated into the concrete terms of any particular situation. I would agree that the public is asking the wrong questions of scientists as a body, but the questions are valid ones when put to an individual scientist and require an answer. If he gives the answer "I acted so because I have no right to betray the will of the nation," then he must also admit that he has no right to act individually as a conscientious objector. Refusal to do scientific work on, for example, the development of atomic weapons is obviously frustrating the will of the nation if its democratically elected government has decided it needs atomic weapons for its defense.

The problem of ethical responsibility for actions that may affect the whole community is not, of course, confined to scientists and, in making provision for conscientious objectors, most Western democracies have accepted the principle that the individual can frustrate the will of the nation. (It is debatable whether the principle would still be accepted if a greater proportion of the population decided to be conscientious objectors.) However, insofar as conscientious objection is allowed in any sphere of action, the responsibility of the individual for the consequences of his actions is greatly increased. And this applies to the scientist in any country where, in spite of economic and other pressures, he still has some measure of freedom to choose the type of work he will do, the results he will publish, and even, if he thinks fit, to decide not to practice science at all.

Ethical problems do not only arise in connection with war, but this is nevertheless the area in which scientists today are likely to find their consciences most troubled. To practice science for the specific purpose of developing weapons involves an ethical judgment that cannot be avoided by trying to cast all responsibility onto those who have to make decisions as to when and where these weapons are used.

Once again I find myself disagreeing with Dr. Bronowski who, in his book *Science and Human Values* (London: Hutchinson, 1961) writes, "Science has nothing to be ashamed of even in the ruins of Nagasaki. The shame is theirs who appeal to other values than the human imaginative values that science has evolved." By "science" he presumably means scientists, since feelings of shame cannot be attributed to an abstraction, but his choice of words, although perhaps unintentional, illustrates a weakness to which we, as scientists, are peculiarly prone. We too easily tend to reject our individual share of responsibility for any consequences of our work about which we may feel uneasy, and pass the responsibility on to "them," by implication usually the politicians, the decision-makers. This is in contrast to the attitude adopted when the results of scientific work are generally accepted as good and where nonscientific administrators and politicians have played their part by making decisions that we happen to believe were right. If there is shame in the ruins of Nagasaki, then it must be borne in part by those who provided the means, even though they may not have decided the ends.

The ethical responsibility of a scientist may be stated plainly as follows. Where the possible uses of the end-product of any scientific work are known, then those scientists doing the work share a part of the responsibility for those uses whether they be good or bad. The scientist, therefore, cannot with an easy conscience escape from the burden of making what may be essentially moral and political decisions about the work he will do and the results he will publish.

Can the scientific discipline guide the individual in making these decisions? How much help can he obtain from the moral component that is "right in the grain of science itself"?

To answer these questions we must distinguish between the two processes that occur in making an ethical decision. First, in deciding upon a course of action, an individual must consider the end which he hopes to achieve. Such ends may range from making himself happy to furthering the greatest happiness of the greatest number, from keeping himself and his family alive to preserving the nation or the human race, from pleasing himself to pleasing God; and the ends he really aims at may often be very different from those he openly proclaims. The practice of science can, in my opinion, give no guidance in this choice of ends. Science has its own ends which are strictly limited. They are the furtherance of man's understanding of himself and his environment and the increase of his power to control and alter that environment. The purposes for which he shall use this understanding and power cannot be decided without some basic hypothesis or faith which is not deducible by the scientific process.

The second aspect of decision-making is the choice of means, and here it would at first sight appear that the scientific method can make a contribution. Scientists are trained to attack the problem "How may such-and-such a result be obtained?" and have achieved undreamt of success in solving such problems in the material world. Nevertheless, the application of scientific techniques to the problems of society and human relationships does not always meet with similar success. The reason for this is that, although we can still observe, collect data, and build hypotheses, we are severely limited in our capacity to experiment under conditions where all the possible variables are strictly controlled. This is not to say that results obtained by the social scientist and psychologist, in conjunction with the anthropologist and the human biologist, may not have great relevance to ethics. But in so many of the major ethical problems facing mankind today, significant scientific results are scanty, experiments cannot be made, and vital decisions cannot be deferred. At the national level we must now act either on the assumption that nuclear weapons will deter aggression, preserve peace, and insure the continued existence of the values we uphold, or we must act on the contrary assumption. If we choose the wrong assumption, then we shall not be in the position of the scientist who may, when his experiment fails to produce the expected results, devise a new experiment to test an alternative hypothesis. The same considerations apply in many of the problems that face us at the personal level. Bringing up our children is an experiment which we have to carry out, but which we can seldom repeat if we judge our first attempt to be a failure.

We have therefore to be guided in our actions and our associated ethical judgments, not by a scientific theory resting on unimpeachable experimentally determined facts, but by a combination of our reason and our beliefs concerning human values and the real source of power in the universe. Dr. Bronowski has argued, and here I agree, that certain values are directly cultivated by the practice of science, namely, truth to fact, freedom of thought and speech, tolerance, dissent, justice, honor, human dignity, and self-respect; and that "if these values did not exist, then the society of scientists would have to invent them to make the practice of science possible." But these values, impressive as they may sound, are, in my view, secondary to those "of tenderness, of kindliness, of human intimacy and love" which, as Dr. Bronowski says, "are not generated by the practice of science." If the latter values are accepted, then the scientific values will automatically follow, and in certain circumstances, the demands of truth, justice, and honor must in fact give way to the greater demand of love. Without love, even freedom of thought and speech, tolerance, and dissent lose their ethical imperative. Here I am no longer attempting an impartial discussion, but, as is inevitable when one talks of values, I am revealing my own particular bias, a belief in the supreme power of love at all levels of human relationships.

The solution of most ethical problems depends finally upon a valuation of individual man in relationships to other men and the community, and upon an estimate of the real sources of power that determine the outcome of these relationships. This is the province of religion, using that term in its widest sense, and it is, I believe, within the context of a religious outlook that the scientist must form his ethical judgments. Science alone is not enough. It is wisdom without compassion. If we, as scientists, fail to recognize this fact, then science itself may fall into disrepute through its lack of success in fields where the power of its method is limited.

TRY THESE PROJECTS FOR—
ETHICS FOR THE SCIENTIST,
by Haybittle

1. *Hold a mock trial or a debate.*

   ■ A scientist who knows his work will help kill and mutilate people, but does it anyway "because the government told me to."

   ■ A military officer carries out orders from a superior officer to commit an act of cruelty and brutality.

   ■ An advertising man knows a product is inferior but creates a brilliant sales campaign for it anyway, because "that's what I'm paid for and, if I don't do it, someone else will."

   ■ A physician prescribes a placebo (a harmless substance) for a patient because "he had nothing physically wrong with him but he wants something for his symptoms and feels better when he's getting medication."

   ■ A judge sentences a convicted man to death because "he was found guilty and that is the law."

2. *Express yourself.*

   ■ Draw up a class resolution about, or write a letter to, one of the people mentioned above in #1.

   ■ Write his answer defending himself.

   ■ Write a first person essay: "A Scientist at War with Himself."

   ■ Write a sermon to be delivered in a synagogue with mostly scientists as members (see if you can base your sermon on an appropriate Bible passage).

3. *Know yourself.*

   Choose a particular scientific profession that interests you greatly or you know a great deal about, and write (or give orally) a book review of either books *Jewish Values and Social Crisis*, by Albert Vorspan (UAHC), and *Justice, Justice*, by Henry Cohen (UAHC), as if you were that kind of scientist. The basic question to answer is: What are you as an individual scientist, and what are scientists as a group, supposed to do about the problems described in the book?

4. *Go creative.*

   Try a "historical reconstruction." Suppose scientists of the world had refused to do any work to develop the atomic bomb, and there were no such bombs in existence. Beginning with the United States having not dropped an atomic

162

bomb on Hiroshima in 1945 during World War II, figure out what would have happened since then that didn't, or what wouldn't have happened that did, or both. Present your results any way you like.

■ Summary chapter in an imaginary book.

■ "Were We Right?"—An imaginary poll of scientists who refused then and are still alive today; or, an interview with one of them.

■ Film, filmstrip, slide set, poster sequence, cartoons, or other illustrative techniques to show contrasting scenes—What's actually happened after the atom bomb, and what would (or could) have happened without it.

5. *Research.*

■ Jewish values—Consult *Jewish Values,* by Louis Jacobs; *The Future of the American Jew,* by Mordecai M. Kaplan, Chapter 15; "Basic Values in Jewish Religion," pp. 246–339.
   Which of the various values you find are universal, true of all peoples? Which distinctively and uniquely Jewish? Which descriptive (actually accepted and lived by most Jews today)? Normative (ideals we ought to try and accept and live by)? Part of the generally accepted American way of life? Conflicting with the generally accepted American way of life? Supported or not contradicted by science? Contradicted or not supported by science?
   The same value, of course, may go under more than one heading. Design a poster chart with 8 columns, each containing a few basic values, to explain your research to the class and leave up for use during discussions.

■ Influencing the mind through chemotheraphy, psychotherapy, hypnotherapy, etc.; differences and similarities. (Resources: Encyclopedias of science and/or psychology.)

■ Read *Brave New World,* by Aldous Huxley. Report on (a) characters and incidents that relate to any of Heitler's or Haybittle's ideas; (b) how well Huxley, writing in 1932, prophesied the future.

■ What is "a drug"? An "ethical drug"? A "patent medicine"? (Resource: Unabridged dictionary.) Do drugs being manufactured today actually meet these definitions? (Resources: Your pharmicist, public relations official of a large drug firm.)

In your report, draw some conclusions about the ethical as well as the physiological implications of what you find out.

AFTER YOU HAVE READ—
ETHICS FOR THE SCIENTIST,
by Haybittle

Discuss these questions:

1. Most people have trouble deciding when to use "moral" and when to use "ethical." Is there any essential difference between them?

2. Haybittle disagrees with this statement by Bronowski: "In assessing collective responsibility we must explain to people that they are asking of scientists quite the wrong collective decision when they say 'you should not have invented this' or 'you should not have disclosed that.' This is asking us all to betray the public . . . by asking scientists to make decisions which are for the nation to make . . . Scientists have no right to betray the will of the nation."

   What do you think? Is Bronowski saying a scientist should do whatever he is called on to do, regardless of his own conscience? If so, compare this statement with another by Bronowski:

   ". . . the individual scientist is the keeper of his private conscience. He has the right to act individually as a conscientious objector. . . . He has a business to settle with his own conscience, the serious business of whether he personally will engage in forms of research of which he does not morally approve."

   Do you agree with Haybittle that Bronowski contradicts himself?

   Where does Edmund R. Leach, the eminent British anthropologist, stand, according to this statement from the *Saturday Evening Post*, November 16, 1968?

   "The moral doubts of those who helped to design the first atomic bombs have become notorious, and today there must be thousands of highly qualified scientists engaged on hundreds of different chemical and biological research projects who face similar difficulties. It is not simply a matter of trying to measure the positive value of a gain in human knowledge against the negative value of powers of military destruction; the merits and demerits of our whole biological history are at stake. It is no good for the scientist to suppose that there is some outside authority who can decide whether his experiments are legitimate or illegitimate. It has become useless to appeal to God against the Devil; the scientist must be the source of his own morality . . ."

   Where do you stand?

   Some of our scientists who helped develop the atomic bomb later regretted their participation in this destructive project. What about our scientists who worked for ten years to help place a man on the moon? Do you think they might ever regret not having put the same time, talent, and energy on solving a social, economic, or medical problem here on earth?

164

3. Haybittle says: ". . . the problem of ethical responsibility for actions that may affect the whole community is not . . . confined to scientists. We are all confronted with ethical problems."

    Select several nonscientific professions—the one you plan to follow, your parents', and others—including just being a parent.

    What ethical responsibility does each profession have for such community problems as conscientious objection, poverty, sex practices, race relations, anti-Semitism, censorship?

4. Haybittle says the scientist too easily tends to reject his individual responsibility for any consequences of his work about which he may feel uneasy and passes the responsibility on to "them"—that is, anyone except himself. Is this true only of scientists? Give specific examples to justify your answer.

5. Questions of purpose, of good/bad or right/wrong in a moral sense, are outside the realm of natural sciences like physics or chemistry. But what about the social sciences like anthropology, sociology, or psychology, which deal with human behavior? Are they interpretative disciplines, or merely descriptive like the natural sciences? Do they provide information that can be used for either good or bad, morally speaking, or do they help guide our moral and ethical choices?

    Compare your answer with the following from Haybittle.

    "We have therefore to be guided in our actions and our associated ethical judgments, not by a scientific theory resting on unimpeachable experimentally determined facts, but by a combination of our reason and our beliefs concerning human values and the real source of power in the universe."

6. Write out your own definitions of these values that Haybittle says are cultivated by the practice of science.
    Stress, if you can, both ethical and scientific elements.
    Freedom of thought and speech.
    Tolerance.
    Dissent.
    Justice.
    Honor.
    Human dignity.
    Self-respect.

7. Certain values not cultivated by the practice of science are, according to Haybittle, more important than the scientific values. List and define them.

8. What are Haybittle's two steps in making an ethical decision? In which of these steps, according to him, can science give us guidance? If you say one

or both, tell how; if you say neither, explain why. Practice on an actual case from your own experience, past or present.

My ethical problem.

What I decided as my first step.

Who or what helped me make this decision.

What I decided as my second step.

Who or what helped me make this decision.

In what realm did your mind, conscience, desires, and will power seem to be working—Science? Religion? Both? Neither? Something else entirely?

9. Try to work out your own definition of love—at any level, for all levels, for anyone or anything at all.

Now, compare your definition with the one implied in this famous commandment:

"Love your neighbor as yourself." (Leviticus 19:19.)

Does "I love you" mean "I want from you" or "I want for you"? Or both? Which answer is the point of this story drawn from chasidic literature?

"Rabbi Moshe Leib of Sassov declared to his disciples: 'I learned how we must truly love our neighbor from a conversation between two villagers which I overheard.

" 'The first said: "Tell me, friend Ivan, do you love me?"

" 'The second said: "I love you deeply."

" 'The first: "Do you know, my friend, what gives me pain?"

" 'The second: "How can I know what gives you pain?"

" 'The first: "If you do not know what gives me pain, how can you say that you truly love me?"

" 'Understand then, my sons,' continued the Sassover, 'to love, truly to love, means to know what brings pain to your comrade.' "

10. Find all the similarities you can between this essay by Haybittle and the previous ones by Ferry and Heitler.

11. Look back now at the "Before You Read" section for this essay. According to Haybittle, the values numbered 1-6 are cultivated by the practice of science, but are secondary; the values numbered 7-12 are not cultivated by the practice of science, and are primary. "If the latter values [7-12] are accepted," he says, "then the scientific values [1-6] will automatically follow, and in certain circumstances, the (former) must in fact give way to the (latter)." Did you number and label them that way ("B" and "S" for values 1-6; "A" and "NS" for values 7-12)? If not, how would you defend your differences from this outstanding physicist?

166

After you've finished Part III, "Science and Ethics," go back over all the "Before You Read" questions so far, including those for Parts I and II. Reconsider your answers and write out your questions, statements, answers, or ideas, as many as you like, under these headings:

1. I've changed my mind about—

2. I still feel the same way I did before about—

3. I feel more certain than before about—

4. I feel less certain than before about—

See suggestions in "Ask Yourself Again" Part I, page 86.

TEACHING MACHINE

i wanted to speak with the machine
  however
neither of us spoke the language of
  the other
hello i said the machine said nothing
clickity click the machine said i said
  nothing
we each brought his own translator
  the next morning
hello i said clickityclick said the
  translator
clickityclick said the machine clickityclick
  said the translator
hello said my translator clickityclick
  said i.

Norman H. Russell

Part IV

SUPPLEMENTARY MATERIAL

"WHAT AM I, LIFE?"

What am I, Life? A thing of watery salt
Held in cohesion by unresting cells,
Which work they know not why, which never halt,
Myself unwitting where their Master dwells.
I do not bid them, yet they toil, they spin;
A world which uses me as I use them,
Nor do I know which end or which begin
Nor which to praise, which pamper, which condemn.
So, like a marvel in a marvel set,
I answer to the vast, as wave by wave
The sea of air goes over, dry or wet,
Or the full moon comes swimming from her cave,
Or the great sun comes north, this myriad I
Tingles, not knowing how, yet wondering why.

John Masefield

Scientists
Are
Stupid!

◆

John W. Campbell

IN AN EXACT and technical sense, scientists are stupid. This does not mean they are foolish, or that they are ignorant; a lot of people rather hopelessly confuse the terms ignorant, foolish, and stupid. A snake is hatched from its egg wise, but stupid—i.e., it is born knowing a great deal, but unable to learn much of anything. A baby, on the other hand, is born ignorant but intelligent—it doesn't know much, but can learn a terrific amount. A new-hatched rattlesnake knows what its prey is, what its enemies are, and how to catch the one and avoid the other. It has an enormous mass of built-in instinctive information.

A human baby doesn't have anywhere near as much wired-in-at-birth information—but it learns from experience.

The reason I say scientists are stupid is that they do not learn from experience. Throughout the history of science, they have repeatedly made one classic goof; they repeat the same weary mistake, generation after generation, and they're still making it. That they *say* they've changed has very poor correlation with what they *do*.

The scientists of Galileo's time—the individuals who had been formally educated to the highest levels of the then-known science of the culture—were the Church officials and astrologers who gave Galileo such a rough time for teaching such fantastic nonsense as that the Earth went around the Sun, instead of vice versa.

The essential blunder science and scientists have repeated down the centuries, is the Hidden Postulate "We know the limits of the possible." They won't come out and say that openly—to a considerable extent, they aren't consciously aware that they are actually using that postulate in their thinking. But lordee me, do they use it!

I am starting my thirtieth year as editor of the science-fiction magazine now called *Analog*, published by Condé-Nast Publishing Co. When I first took it over, it was called *Astounding Stories*, and was published by Street and Smith Publishing Co. (which company later merged with Condé-Nast).

That was in 1937. If you can remember that far back, there were no rocketships, atomic power didn't exist, transistors weren't imagined, the superduper special Schneider Cup ultra-fast racing planes were doing around 400 miles an hour (commercial transports that slow are used only on backwoods feeder lines now), and antibiotics were unknown. Television was, we were assured, just around the corner. (They were trying to do it with mechanical scanning discs.)

I'd had some trouble with my professors at MIT, who did *not* approve of my writing that "pseudo-science," that "science-fantasy nonsense" (which I'd started in my freshman year; I wanted one of those grand new Model A Fords; it cost two novelettes and part of a novel). The only one of my MIT professors who liked science-fiction and helped me with some highly interesting story ideas, was a man not very well known at that time—a fellow by the name of Norbert Weiner, who seemed interested in science-fiction thinking about mathematical robots. It was a good many years later that Dr. Weiner invented the term *cybernetics,* but he did *not* belong to the group of stupid scientists. He did believe that there was a great deal more to this Universe than Man had yet discovered.

But science-fiction was still being totally rejected as fantasy—nonsense—Sunday-supplement exaggerations . . .

In 1930, Dr. Forest Ray Moulton, one of America's greatest astronomers and astrophysicists, wrote a college textbook *Astronomy* in which he said, in discussing meteorites, that there had been many romances written about voyages between the planets, but that anyone who knew anything about the real physical forces operating between the planets knew that such voyages were *forever* impossible.

This was several years after Dr. Goddard had built and flown his first liquid-fueled rockets.

Of course, Dr. Goddard's work was pretty thoroughly ignored in this country. It was after the Germans had taught the Allies that rockets of frightening power could be built that anyone really paid attention to the idea. And even so, it was the Russians who first demonstrated that Dr. Moulton was really stupid—he had done precisely what Galileo's persecutors had done. He, too, thought he knew the total nature of the Universe so well he could state what was *forever* impossible. What could *never* be done.

The United States finally got around to paying royalties on Dr. Goddard's original liquid-fuel rockets patents to Dr. Goddard's widow. Only after that could they acknowledge that Dr. Goddard had been a great pioneer, and honor him with a posthumous gold medal in 1960.

For some reason scientists find it much easier to honor a man who's safely dead, and no longer competing with them. Gregor Mendel, for instance, was most thoroughly rejected when he introduced the idea of genetics—and, more important even than that tremendous idea, perhaps, Mendel was also responsible for introducing the techniques of statistical analysis into the life sciences. His work wasn't accepted for some forty years, after he was long dead.

The scientists of Mendel's time *knew* that mathematics could not be applied to biological problems, and that, therefore, the concepts of genetics Mendel had derived by statistical analysis were nonsense.

Science-fiction was "pseudo-science" and "science-fantasy" because it kept talking about things that scientists, real scientists like Dr. Moulton, *knew* were impossible. Things like spaceships going to Mars and Venus, and men landing on the Moon. Or atomic power plants, and atomic bombs. Sheer, impossible nonsense.

Scientists are stupid because they repeat and repeat and repeat the same weary goof. "We *know* that's impossible nonsense!"

For uncounted centuries farmers and seamen—who are acutely interested in weather phenomena—have stated as observational experience that the phases of the Moon influence Earth's weather. And for some hundred and fifty years scientists have rejected this superstition, this folklore nonsense.

A couple of years ago some not-so-thoroughly convinced meteorologists, with the aid of a man who's a hobby astronomer and a member of the Society of Variable Star Observers and knew something about the motions of Earth, Moon, and Sun, teamed up with an electronic computer. Using weather data from all over the United States, over a fifty-year period, they conclusively demonstrated that the Moon's phases *did* correlate with Earth's heavy rainfalls.

Scientists have, of course, pretty solidly rejected the studies made on ESP—Extra Sensory Perception. That's folklore and superstition, and anything that's labeled "folklore" is automatically wrong as everybody knows, of course. (Labels have that power; it can be very comforting when you don't want to recognize something.)

Dr. Rhine didn't get very far, because the standard theories of scientists showed that it could not happen—as impossible as Moulton knew spaceships going to other planets would be.

However, Professor Willem Tenhaeff, a thoroughly hardheaded Dutchman at the University of Utrecht, in the Netherlands, has a much more pragmatic approach than Dr. Rhine had. Instead of presenting masses of statistics and esoteric arguments based on mathematical theorems so complex that most mathematicians can't be sure of themselves, and no general public could follow—Dr. Tenhaeff is simply making valuable, practical *use* of ESP-talented clairvoyants. His approach is more or less "I see no point in arguing about whether or not the faculty exists—we'll ignore that question. Because we can *use* it. That's useful and valuable; later we can argue about whether it exists."

Dr. Tenhaeff has some forty talented clairvoyants he works with. Maybe they don't really have ESP—maybe it's just subconscious reasoning from normally unnoticed clues, or any other rationalization you prefer. But they've been of great help to police in catching smugglers, locating lost children, identifying murderers, and predicting where an escaped madman *will be*. (It's really not too helpful to be told where he *is*; by the time you get there, he'll be elsewhere. Tenhaeff's clairvoyants repeatedly tell the police where the sought-for individual *will be* at a future time.)

ESP may not exist—but whatever those talented individuals Tenhaeff has found have . . . it works.

I've read a number of books on an old standard science-fiction theme, written in recent years by first rank professional scientists; communication with extra-terrestrial alien intelligences is now a respectable field of speculation and discussion. Very interesting books. That life can exist and achieve intelligence elsewhere in the Universe is now a perfectly sound scientific proposition.

It was, of course, "pseudo-science nonsense" a few years ago, fit only for science-fiction.

But scientific stupidity is still with us; all of those speculative books are still *sure* that interstellar travel at speeds faster than light are "forever impossible"—just as Moulton was sure interplanetary travel was.

They are equally sure that if interplanetary communication is ever achieved, it can only be done by radio or laser light beams. There is absolutely no other method possible.

Now that can be called either "gross stupidity" or "incredible arrogance." Will scientists never learn that they don't, and can't, know all the possibilities in this Universe? It's the same old, repeatedly repeated goof—"We know the absolute limits of the possible now, and no one can ever go beyond!"

So we know of no possible method of exceeding the speed of light, and our theories say it's inherently impossible forever.

Man has had something that could vaguely be called science for about three thousand years. We've had real, hard experimental science only about one-tenth that long. To the best of present astrophysical knowledge, the Sun and solar system are about five billion years old. And our Sun and planets are made of the dust and gases that were "cooked" in some far greater cosmic cooker for millions of years—a gigantic star perhaps twenty to a hundred times as big as our Sun. That star "burned" hydrogen by fusion reactions to produce the heavy elements such as iron, silver, gold—all the heavier elements—that we know—and then exploded in an explosion of truly inconceivable violence. The dust and debris of that explosion eventually went to make up our Sun and probably a few others, some five billion years ago.

So our system is a second-generation system, made up of "used parts" from a far older star.

But there are stars which are believed to be *twenty* billion years old. Those stars could have fostered life on their planets, life that evolved intelligence, built civilization, discovered interplanetary flight, atomic energy, all the things we know, *fifteen billion years ago.* Fifteen thousand million years ago, they could have had all the science we know now.

And our puling infant science has the colossal gall to say they know what such a science could and could not do? A science so primitive that it can't even explain things that human beings themselves do every day? That can't even define what "to think" means? That can't cure a simple problem like the common cold is fit to lay down the limits of what a race a billion years older may have done? *They* may have science and scientific research that has developed for five hundred times longer than the entire history of hominids on Earth—not merely *homo sapiens'* brief half-million year history.

The rate of accomplishment under the drive of conscious, planned research is another thing scientists are stupid about. We are progressing at a rate fantastically greater than we are aware of—and men overlook the implications of that.

Perhaps the best way to explain that is to use the science-fiction approach; let's consider a little science-fiction plot outline.

Suppose that a drone reconnaissance plane has been flown through the latest Chinese nuclear bomb cloud, collecting samples for analysis. It was sent from a base on Guam, and the on-board computer control system was programmed to return the plane to Guam. But . . . something happened somehow, and the drone fell through a time warp, on its way back, and was suddenly in 1930 instead of 1967, back about the time I started writing "that science-fantasy nonsense." The on-board computer and position-sensor mechanisms manage to reorient correctly, and the plane comes in and finally lands on Guam in 1930, on the last gasp of its fuel. (It was programmed for radio-controlled landing, but when it sent out its "here I am" signals on 2200 megacycles to alert Ground Control, nobody took control; it circled until the fuel exhaustion caused the computer to cut over to the emergency program, and it landed by on-board radar-computer guidance.)

There is, of course, more than merely frantic interest in this incredible machine when the Army Air Corps gets hold of it. It's shipped back to the United States under the toppest of top secret classification, and scientists descend on it for study.

The markings are clearly U.S. Army Air Corps insignia, but with very evident changes—apparently the Air Corps has been renamed the Air Force. But whatever the source, it's quickly determined that it must be centuries, if not millennia, in the future.

The engine, for instance. They couldn't know it of course, but the thing has a ram-jet engine which won't begin to function below 300 miles per hour. Since no plane on Earth as of 1930 could have boosted that drone to any such speed, even if they'd known they couldn't have done anything about it. They can readily spot the fuel tank—it's still got traces of kerosene, not gasoline in it—and the pipes that obviously are meant to lead fuel to spray-jets in a piece of large pipe on top of the machine. Open pipe, open at both ends, however, and obviously it makes no sense whatever. When fuel is put in the tank, and made to flow into the big pipe, it has to be doused quickly, because the whole precious machine nearly catches on fire, and there isn't a sign of any engine action.

The airframe team is going frantic in about the same degree the engine and propulsion team is. They can't understand the structure any better than the power plant team can figure out the engine. For one thing, they were fortunate in that they made some tests on the metal after unbolting one section of it. Every effort to drill or cut the stuff—a completely strange grayish metal, much lighter than steel, yet stronger—ruined their tools. Even the newly discovered tungsten carbide tools failed rapidly on the tough, stubborn stuff. Chemists identified it as an alloy of titanium, a not rare, but extremely intractable metal. But the chemists didn't have adequate warning of titanium's properties. Since the drills and saws were ruined so quickly, they tried a cutting torch. The metal caught fire and burned with a blindingly brilliant white light—and the fire absolutely could not be extinguished. Water made it burn explosively—sand wouldn't stop it. It burned with a brilliant but smoky flame in carbon dioxide, and just as ferociously in pure nitrogen as in air! They were just as lucky that they'd completely detached the piece before they tried the cutting torch, or the entire machine would have been lost.

The shape of the thing—a sort of pinched-waist shape—makes no sense to them. (It was designed for supersonic flight, and has the "Coke bottle shape" which was of course unknown in the '30s.)

At this point, the physicists who were studying samples from the structure sound off with howls of dismay and horror. It's radioactive. Dangerously so. But far worse than that—it's radioactive with absolutely and totally impossible kinds of radioactive materials. There's radioactive *aluminum!* And radioactive cobalt and silver and practically half the elements in the table. And that's absolutely impossible; it's known for an absolute fact that those elements are *not* radioactive. No light element such as aluminum or silicon is—only things like radium and uranium. (The neutron wasn't discovered until 1932; only then were synthetic radioactive elements possible.)

Meanwhile the Signal Corps people have been trying to make some sense out of some of the electronics on board.

They can't, of course. The computer is a beautiful piece of submicrominiaturized solid-state digital equipment, with a 2-nanosecond pulse time.

There wasn't a piece of equipment on Earth at that time that could have detected the one- to two-volt signals that lasted for only two-billionths of a second, even if they *had* had some way of making a connection to the circuits that could be seen only with power microscopes. And those parts were merely interconnections; the real active elements of the circuit were grown-crystal devices that could be recognized only by someone who knew how they were built.

The radar equipment, operating on 30,000 megacycles, would be utterly beyond recognition. The queer square plumbing pipes that went from here to there, carrying nothing, open to the atmosphere would mean nothing to them. They hadn't a hint of radar-type microwave wave guides then. The only equipment they'd be able to recognize would be the "ultra-high-frequency amplifier system"—which was, in fact, the low-frequency amplifier chain of the radar IF system. It operated at 50 megacycles—a frequency some advanced laboratory equipment of the time could barely reach.

The whole equipment—from transistors to wave guides to miniaturized gas-turbine power generator—would be completely unintelligible to them. They couldn't even learn anything from the equipment; there would be far too many missing steps. Their chemists couldn't analyze the silicon in the power transistors and get the right answers—they didn't have chemical reagents pure enough to make a meaningful analysis possible. They couldn't do *anything* with it!

They would have run into things they *knew* were impossible. Told authoritatively that the solid-state devices did in fact have thus-and-such functions, and were made of silicon with trace impurities, they could have proven that was untrue, because when they built devices precisely as described, no such functions appeared.

They couldn't come even close to the necessary purity of silicon, and they certainly didn't know how to grow silicon crystals. Of course they wouldn't function.

They *knew* aluminum couldn't possibly be radioactive.

If the sampling chamber of the drone had picked up some of the bomb debris, the chemists might have recognized uranium—but they wouldn't have detected neptunium, plutonium, or any of the other transuranic elements. All the transuranics have very similar chemical properties, and you can't recognize their separate identities unless you know how to look for them—which, naturally, they did not. The teflon insulation on some of the equipment would have driven the organic chemists to distraction—they could analyze it, but it's impossible to make such a compound. Even the polyethylene would give them nervous twitches; it was made under a pressure of 50,000 pounds per square inch and, in 1930, nobody could process gases at any such impossible pressure.

If forced to guess how far in the future that drone came from, I doubt that they'd have guessed anything less than 500 years.

And our 300-year-old science presumes to know how all intelligent beings throughout all space *have* to do things, and knows what they can't possibly ever do?

They can only use radio and/or light beams?

Science can have more rational right to make such statements when it can define what that ESP talent is, for instance. Maybe, right now, we're living in oblivious unawareness while the Intergalactic Communications Corporation is driving commercial and entertainment telepathy broadcasts all through this volume of space. We wouldn't notice that any more than the 1930 Signal Corps could have detected the 30,000 megacycle radio waves the drone's radar system was bouncing off the landing field.

Sure . . . there are some things that are impossible, and always will be. Nobody can ever make a four-sided triangle, but that's simply by reason of definitions. If it doesn't have three sides, then it's not a triangle, by definition.

But don't try to say that no intelligent being can ever exceed the speed of light.

You're much to ignorant to make such all-embracing statements; you're definitely being a stupid scientist if you do. Somebody with a culture that's had high-level science for the last one or two billion years might be sufficiently amused by your colossal arrogance to give you a demonstration.

And certainly the record so far established by scientists is remarkably consistent; they've goofed high, wide, and handsome for the last three centuries, all the way from Galileo through Goddard!

The Bird
and
the Machine

Loren Eiseley

I SUPPOSE THEIR LITTLE bones have years ago been lost among the stones and winds of those high glacial pastures. I suppose their feathers blew eventually into the piles of tumbleweed beneath the straggling cattle fences and rotted there in the mountain snows, along with dead steers and all the other things that drift to an end in the corners of the wire. I do not quite know why I should be thinking of birds over the *New York Times* at breakfast, particularly the birds of my youth half a continent away. It is a funny thing what the brain will do with memories and how it will treasure them and finally bring them into odd juxtapositions with other things, as though it wanted to make a design, or get some meaning out of them, whether you want it or not, or even see it.

It used to seem marvelous to me, but I read now that there are machines that can do these things in a small way, machines that can crawl about like animals, and that it may not be long now until they do more things—maybe even make themselves—I saw that piece in the *Times* just now. And then they will, maybe—well, who knows—but you read about it more and more with no one making any protest, and already they can add better than we and reach up and hear things through the dark and finger the guns over the night sky.

This is the new world that I read about at breakfast. This is the world that confronts me in my biological books and journals, until there are times when I sit quietly in my chair and try to hear the little purr of the cogs in my head and the tubes flaring and dying as the messages go through them and the circuits snap shut or open. This is the great age, make no mistake about it; the robot has been born somewhat appropriately along with the atom bomb, and the brain they say now is just another type of more complicated feedback system. The engineers have its basic principles worked out; it's mechanical, you know; nothing to get superstitious about; and man can always improve on nature once he gets the idea. Well, he's got it all right and that's why, I guess, that I sit here in my chair, with the article crunched in my hand, remembering those two birds and that blue mountain sunlight. There is another magazine article on my desk that reads "Machines Are Getting Smarter Every Day." I don't deny it, but I'll still stick with the birds. It's life I believe in, not machines.

Maybe you don't believe there is any difference. A skeleton is all joints and pulleys, I'll admit. And when man was in his simpler stages of machine building in the eighteenth century, he quickly saw the resemblances. "What," wrote Hobbes, "is the heart but a spring, and the nerves but so many strings, and the joints but so many wheels, giving motion to the whole body?" Tinkering about in their shops it was inevitable in the end that men would see the world as a huge machine "subdivided into an infinite number of lesser machines."

The idea took on with a vengeance. Little automatons toured the country—dolls controlled by clockwork. Clocks described as little worlds were taken on tours by their designers. They were made up of moving figures, shifting scenes, and other remarkable devices. The life of the cell was unknown. Man, whether he was conceived as possessing a soul or not, moved and jerked about like these tiny puppets. A human being thought of himself in terms of his own tools and implements. He had been fashioned like the puppets he produced and was only a more clever model made by a greater designer.

Then in the nineteenth century, the cell was discovered, and the single machine in its turn was found to be the product of millions of infinitesimal machines—the cells. Now, finally, the cell itself dissolves away into an abstract chemical machine—and that into some intangible, inexpressible flow of energy. The secret seems to lurk all about, the wheels get smaller and smaller, and they turn more rapidly, but when you try to seize it the life is gone—and so, by popular definition, some would say that life was never there in the first place. The wheels and the cogs are the secret and we can make them better in time—machines that will run faster and more accurately than real mice to real cheese.

I have no doubt it can be done, though a mouse harvesting seeds on an autumn thistle is to me a fine sight and more complicated, I think, in his multiform activity, than a machine "mouse" running a maze. Also, I like to think of the possible shape of the future brooding in mice, just as it brooded once in a rather ordinary mousy insectivore who became a man. It leaves a nice fine indeterminate sense of wonder that even an electronic brain hasn't got, because you know perfectly well that if the electronic brain changes, it will be because of something man has done to it. But what man will do to himself he doesn't really know. A certain scale of time and a ghostly intangible thing called change are ticking in him. Powers and potentialities like the oak in the seed, or a red and awful ruin. Either way, it's impressive; and the mouse has it, too. Or those birds, I'll never forget those birds—yet before I measured their significance, I learned the lesson of time first of all. I was young then and left alone in a great desert—part of an expedition that had scattered its men over several hundred miles in order to carry on research more effectively. I learned there that time is a series of planes existing superficially in the same universe. The tempo is a human illusion, a subjective clock ticking in our own kind of protoplasm.

As the long months passed, I began to live on the slower planes and to observe more readily what passed for life there. I sauntered, I passed more and more slowly up and down the canyons in the dry baking heat of midsummer. I slumbered for long hours in the shade of huge brown boulders that had gathered in tilted companies out on the flats. I had forgotten the world of men and the world had forgotten me. Now and then I found a skull in the canyons, and these justified my remaining there. I took a serene cold interest in these discoveries. I had come, like many a naturalist before me, to view life with a wary and subdued attention. I had grown to take pleasure in the divested bone.

I sat once on a high ridge that fell away before me into a waste of sand dunes. I sat through hours of a long afternoon. Finally, as I glanced beside my boot an indistinct configuration caught my eye. It was a coiled rattlesnake, a big one. How long he had sat with me I do not know. I had not frightened him. We were both locked in the sleep-walking tempo of the earlier world, baking in the same high air and sunshine. Perhaps he had been there when I came. He slept on as I left, his coils, so ill discerned by me, dissolving once more among the stones and gravel from which I had barely made him out.

Another time I got on a higher ridge, among some tough little wind-warped pines half covered over with sand in a basin-like depression that caught everything carried by the air up to those heights. There were a few thin bones of birds, some cracked shells of indeterminable age, and the knotty fingers of pine roots bulged out of shape from their long and agonizing grasp upon the crevices of the rock. I lay under the pines in the sparse shade and went to sleep once more.

It grew cold finally, for autumn was in the air by then, and the few things that lived thereabouts were sinking down into an even chillier scale of time. In the moments between sleeping and waking I saw the roots about me and slowly, slowly, a foot in what seemed many centuries, I moved my sleep-stiffened hands over the scaling bark and lifted my numbed face after the vanishing sun. I was a great awkward thing of knots and aching limbs, trapped up there in some long, patient endurance that involved the necessity of putting living fingers into rock and by slow, aching expansion bursting those rocks asunder. I suppose, so thin and slow was the time of my pulse by then, that I might have stayed on to drift still deeper into the lower cadences of the frost, or the crystalline life that glistens pebbles, or shines in a snowflake, or dreams in the meteoric iron between the worlds.

It was a dim descent, but time was present in it. Somewhere far down in that scale the notion struck me that one might come the other way. Not many months thereafter I joined some colleagues heading higher into a remote windy tableland

181

where huge bones were reputed to protrude like boulders from the turf. I had drowsed with reptiles and moved with the century-long pulse of trees; now, lethargically, I was climbing back up some invisible ladder of quickening hours. There had been talk of birds in connection with my duties. Birds are intense, fast-living creatures—reptiles, I suppose one might say, that have escaped out of the heavy sleep of time, transformed fairy creatures dancing over sunlit meadows. It is a youthful fancy, no doubt, but because of something that happened up there among the escarpments of that range, it remains with me a life-long impression. I can never bear to see a bird imprisoned.

We came into that valley through the trailing mists of a spring night. It was a place that looked as though it might never have known the foot of man, but our scouts had been ahead of us and we knew all about the abandoned cabin of stone that lay far up on one hillside. It had been built in the land rush of the last century and then lost to the cattlemen again as the marginal soils failed to take to the plow.

There were spots like this all over that country. Lost graves marked by unlettered stones and old corroding rim-fire cartridge cases lying where somebody had made a stand among the boulders that rimmed the valley. They are all that remain of the range wars; the men are under the stones now. I could see our cavalcade winding in and out through the mist below us. Torches, the reflection of the truck lights on our collecting tins, and the far-off bumping of a loose dinosaur thigh bone in the bottom of a trailer. I stood on a rock a moment looking down and thinking what it cost in money and equipment to capture the past.

We had, in addition, instructions to lay hands on the present. The word had come through to get them alive—birds, reptiles, anything. A zoo somewhere abroad needed restocking. It was one of those reciprocal matters in which science involves itself. Maybe our museum needed a stray ostrich egg and this was the payoff. Anyhow, my job was to help capture some birds and that was why I was there before the trucks.

The cabin had not been occupied for years. We intended to clean it out and live in it, but there were holes in the roof and the birds had come in and were roosting in the rafters. You could depend on it in a place like this where everything blew away, and even a bird needed some place out of the weather and away from coyotes. A cabin going back to nature in a wild place draws them till they come in, listening at the eaves, I imagine, pecking softly among the shingles till they find a hole and then suddenly the place is theirs and man is forgotten.

Sometimes of late years I find myself thinking the most beautiful sight in the world might be the birds taking over New York after the last man has run away to the hills. I will never live to see it, of course, but I know just how it will sound because I've lived up high and I know the sort of watch birds keep on us. I've listened to sparrows tapping tentatively on the outside of air conditioners when

182

they thought no one was listening, and I know how other birds test the vibrations that come up to them through the television aerials.

"Is he gone?" they ask, and the vibrations come up from below, "Not yet, not yet."

Well, to come back, I got the door open softly and I had the spotlight all ready to turn on and blind whatever birds there were so they couldn't see to get out through the roof. I had a short piece of ladder to put against the far wall where there was a shelf on which I expected to make the biggest haul. I had all the information I needed just like any skilled assassin. I pushed the door open, the hinges squeaking only a little. A bird or two stirred—I could hear them—but nothing flew and there was a faint starlight through the holes in the roof.

I padded across the floor, got the ladder up and the light ready, and slithered up the ladder till my head and arms were over the shelf. Everything was dark as pitch except for the starlight at the little place back of the shelf near the eaves. With the light to blind them, they'd never make it. I had them. I reached my arm carefully over in order to be ready to seize whatever was there and I put the flash on the edge of the shelf where it would stand by itself when I turned it on. That way I'd be able to use both hands.

Everything worked perfectly except for one detail—I didn't know what kind of birds were there. I never thought about it at all, and it wouldn't have mattered if I had. My orders were to get something interesting. I snapped on the flash and sure enough there was a great beating and feathers flying, but instead of my having them, they, or rather he, had me. He had my hand, that is, and for a small hawk not much bigger than my fist he was doing all right. I heard him give one short metallic cry when the light went on and my hand descended on the bird beside him; after that he was busy with his claws and his beak was sunk in my thumb. In the struggle I knocked the lamp over on the shelf, and his mate got her sight back and whisked neatly through the hole in the roof and off among the stars outside. It all happened in fifteen seconds and you might think I would have fallen down the ladder, but no, I had a professional assassin's reputation to keep up, and the bird, of course, made the mistake of thinking the hand was the enemy and not the eyes behind it. He chewed my thumb up pretty effectively and lacerated my hand with his claws, but in the end I got him, having two hands to work with.

He was a sparrow hawk and a fine young male in the prime of life. I was sorry not to catch a pair of them, but as I dripped blood and folded his wings carefully, holding him by the back so that he couldn't strike again, I had to admit the two of them might have been more than I could have handled under the circumstances. The little fellow had saved his mate by diverting me, and that was that. He was born to it, and made no outcry now, resting in my hand hopelessly, but peering toward me in the shadows behind the lamp with a fierce, almost indifferent glance. He neither gave nor expected mercy and something out of the high air passed from him to me, stirring a faint embarrassment.

I quit looking into that eye and managed to get my huge carcass with its fist full of prey back down the ladder. I put the bird in a box too small to allow him to injure himself by struggle and walked out to welcome the arriving trucks. It had been a long day, and camp still to make in the darkness. In the morning that bird would be just another episode. He would go back with the bones in the truck to a small cage in a city where he would spend the rest of his life. And a good thing, too. I sucked my aching thumb and spat out some blood. An assassin has to get used to these things. I had a professional reputation to keep up.

In the morning, with the change that comes on suddenly in that high country, the mist that had hovered below us in the valley was gone. The sky was a deep blue, and one could see for miles over the high outcroppings of stone. I was up early and brought the box in which the little hawk was imprisoned out onto the grass where I was building a cage. A wind as cool as a mountain spring ran over the grass and stirred my hair. It was a fine day to be alive. I looked up and all around and at the hole in the cabin roof out of which the other little hawk had fled. There was no sign of her anywhere that I could see.

"Probably in the next county by now," I thought cynically, but before beginning work I decided I'd have a look at my last night's capture.

Secretively, I looked again all around the camp and up and down and opened the box. I got him right out in my hand with his wings folded properly and I was careful not to startle him. He lay limp in my grasp and I could feel his heart pound under the feathers but he only looked beyond me and up.

I saw him look that last look away beyond me into a sky so full of light that I could not follow his gaze. The little breeze flowed over me again, and nearby a mountain aspen shook all its tiny leaves. I suppose I must have had an idea then of what I was going to do, but I never let it come up into consciousness. I just reached over and laid the hawk on the grass.

He lay there a long minute without hope, unmoving, his eyes still fixed on that blue vault above him. It must have been that he was already so far away in heart that he never felt the release from my hand. He never even stood. He just lay with his breast against the grass.

In the next second after that long minute he was gone. Like a flicker of light, he had vanished with my eyes full on him, but without actually seeing even a premonitory wing beat. He was gone straight into that towering emptiness of light and crystal that my eyes could scarcely bear to penetrate. For another long moment there was silence. I could not see him. The light was too intense. Then from far up somewhere a cry came ringing down.

I was young then and had seen little of the world, but when I heard that cry my heart turned over. It was not the cry of the hawk I had captured; for, by shifting my position against the sun, I was now seeing further up. Straight out of the sun's eye, where she must have been soaring restlessly above us for untold hours, hurtled his mate. And from far up, ringing from peak to peak of the summits over us, came a cry of such unutterable and ecstatic joy that it sounds down across the years and tingles among the cups on my quiet breakfast table.

I saw them both now. He was rising fast to meet her. They met in a great soaring gyre that turned to a whirling circle and a dance of wings. Once more, just once, their two voices, joined in a harsh wild medley of question and response, struck and echoed against the pinnacles of the valley. Then they were gone forever somewhere into those upper regions beyond the eyes of men.

I am older now, and sleep less, and have seen most of what there is to see and am not very much impressed any more, I suppose, by anything. "What Next in the Attributes of Machines?" my morning headline runs. "It Might Be the Power to Reproduce Themselves."

I lay the paper down and across my mind a phrase floats insinuatingly: "It does not seem that there is anything in the construction, constituents, or behavior of the human being which it is essentially impossible for science to duplicate and synthesize. On the other hand . . ."

All over the city the cogs in the hard, bright mechanisms have begun to turn. Figures move through computers, names are spelled out, a thoughtful machine selects the fingerprints of a wanted criminal from an array of thousands. In the laboratory an electronic mouse runs swiftly through a maze toward the cheese it can neither taste nor enjoy. On the second run it does better than a living mouse.

"On the other hand . . ." Ah, my mind takes up, on the other hand the machine does not bleed, ache, hang for hours in the empty sky in a torment of hope to learn the fate of another machine, nor does it cry out with joy nor dance in the air with the fierce passion of a bird. Far off, over a distance greater than space, that remote cry from the heart of heaven makes a faint buzzing among my breakfast dishes and passes on and away.

Can
the World
Be Saved?

LaMont C. Cole

M Y TITLE here is not my first choice. A year or so ago, a physicist discussing some of the same subjects beat me to the use of the title I would have preferred: "Is There Intelligent Life on Earth?" There is evidence that the answer to both questions is in the negative.

In recent years, we have heard much discussion of distinct and nearly independent cultures within our society that fail to communicate with each other—natural scientists and social scientists, for example. The particular failure of communication I am concerned with here is that between ecologists on the one hand and, on the other, those who consider that continuous growth is desirable—growth of population, industry, trade, and agriculture. Put another way, it is the dichotomy between the thinkers and the doers—those who insist that man should try to know the consequences of his actions before he takes them versus those who want to get on with the building of dams and canals, the straightening of river channels, the firing of nuclear explosives, and the industrialization of backward countries.

The message that the ecologists—the "thinkers," if you will—seek to impart could hardly be more urgent or important. It is that man, in the process of seeking a "better way of life," is destroying the natural environment that is essential to any kind of human life at all; that, during his time on earth, man has made giant strides in the direction of ruining the arable land upon which his food supply depends, fouling the air he must breathe and the water he must drink, and upsetting the delicate chemical and climatic balances upon which his very existence depends. And there is all too little indication that man has any intention of mending his ways.

The aspect of this threat to human life that has received the least public attention, but which is, I believe, the most serious is the manner in which we are altering the biological, geological, and chemical cycles upon which life depends.

When the world was young, it did not have the gaseous atmosphere that now surrounds our planet. The water that fills the oceans and furnishes our precipitation and the nitrogen that makes up most of our atmosphere were contained in the rocks formed in the earth's creation. They escaped by various degassing processes, the most dramatic of which was volcanic action.

The amount of oxygen in the atmosphere was negligible before the origin of living organisms that could carry on photosynthesis of the type characterizing green plants, which during daylight hours take in carbon dioxide and give off oxygen. At first, there was virtually no accumulation of oxygen in the atmosphere. The oxygen produced by marine organisms was used by a combination of natural biogeochemical processes which are still operative today—the liberation of incompletely oxidized iron salts in the weathering of silicate rocks and the decomposition of organic matter. But very gradually, some dead organisms began to pass out of circulation by being deposited in sedimentary rocks where some of them became the raw material for the creation of coal and oil. The oxygen that these well-buried organisms would have used up, had they remained on the surface and been subject to decomposition, was allowed to remain in the atmosphere. And eventually, perhaps not until 400 million years ago, this unused oxygen brought the level of oxygen in the atmosphere to slightly over twenty per cent.

This is the same percentage of oxygen in the atmosphere today. Apparently, the combination of green plants and oxygen-using organisms, including animals, became very efficient at taking oxygen from the atmosphere and returning it at equal rates. And this is true in spite of the fact that photosynthesis stops during the hours of darkness and practically stops during winter on land areas in high latitudes. It does continue, however, in low latitudes (although often greatly reduced by seasonal drought) and in the ocean (where marine microorganisms suspended in water produce 70 per cent or more of the world's photosynthetic oxygen). And we have been fortunate that atmospheric circulation patterns move the air about the globe in such a way that we have not had to be concerned that man would run out of oxygen to breathe at night or in winter. As we shall see, man is today pushing his luck.

Another chemical element essential to life is carbon. Plants use carbon dioxide to build their organic compounds, and animals combine the organic compounds with oxygen to obtain the energy for their activities. And all this is possible only because, millions of years ago, the deposition of organic matter in sedimentary rocks led to the creation of a reservoir of oxygen in the atmosphere.

The carbon-oxygen relationship is essential to photosynthesis and thus to the maintenance of all life. But should this relationship be altered, should the balance between the two be upset, life as we know it would be impossible. Man's actions today are bringing this imbalance upon us.

The carbon dioxide in the atmosphere is created in large measure by combustion. Before the time of man, the combustion in the earth's forests was spontaneous. Early man set forest fires to drive game and burned timber for warmth; he went on to find other uses for combustion and to find new combustible materials. First it was coal for heat and power, then oil and natural gas. The exploitation of these so-called fossil fuels made it possible for more people to exist on earth simultaneously than has ever been possible before. It also brought about our present dilemma: The oceans are the world's great reservoir of carbon, taking carbon dioxide from the atmosphere and precipitating it as limestone; we are now adding carbon dioxide to the atmosphere more rapidly than the oceans can assimilate it. Industrial facilities, automobiles, and private homes are the big consumers of fossil fuels, but to appreciate the magnitude of the problem, consider very briefly a still minor source of atmospheric pollution, the airplane, which may have disproportionate importance because much of the carbon dioxide and water vapor produced by the combustion in its engines are released at high altitudes, where they are only slowly removed from the atmosphere.

When you burn a ton of petroleum hydrocarbon, you obtain as by-products about one and a third tons of water and about twice this amount of carbon dioxide. A Boeing 707 in flight accomplishes this feat about every ten minutes. I read in the papers that 10,000 airplanes per week land in New York City alone, not including military aircraft. If we assume very crudely that the 707 is typical of these airplanes, and that its average flight takes four hours, this amounts to an annual release of about 36 million tons of carbon dioxide. And not all flights have a terminus in New York.

Thus the amount of carbon dioxide put into the atmosphere is rising at an ever-rising rate. At the same time, we are removing vast tracts of land from the cycle of photosynthetic production—in this country alone, nearly a million acres of green plants are paved under each year. The loss of these plants is drastically reducing the rate at which oxygen enters the atmosphere. And we do not even know to what extent we are inhibiting photosynthesis through pollution of freshwater and marine environments.

The carbon-oxygen balance is tipping. When, and if, we reach the point at which the rate of combustion exceeds the rate of photosynthesis, we shall start running out of oxygen. If this occurred gradually, its effect would be approximately the same as moving everyone to a mountaintop—a change that might help to alleviate the population crisis by raising death rates. However, the late Lloyd Berkner, director of the Graduate Research Center of the Southwest, thought atmospheric depletion might occur suddenly.

The increase in the proportion of carbon dioxide in the atmosphere will have other effects. Carbon dioxide and water vapor are more transparent to short-wave solar radiation than to the long-wave heat radiation from the earth to space. Thus the increased proportion of these substances in the atmosphere tends to bring about a rise in the earth's surface temperature, the so-called greenhouse effect, altering climates in ways that are still highly controversial in the scientific community but that everyone agrees are undesirable.

One school holds that the increase in temperature will melt the icecaps of Greenland and the Antarctic, raising the sea level by as much as three hundred feet and thereby obliterating most of the major cities of the world. Another school believes that higher temperatures will bring about an increase in evaporation and with it a sharp rise in precipitation; the additional snow falling upon the icecaps will start the glaciers moving again, and another Ice Age will be upon us.

And these represent only the lesser-known effects of combustion on the world. They do not include the direct hazards from air pollution—on man's lungs, for example, or on vegetation near some kinds of industrial plants. Nor do they include the possibility suggested by some scientists that we will put enough smoke particles into the air to block solar radiation, causing a dangerous decrease in the earth's temperature. Just to indicate the complexity and uncertainty of what we are doing to the earth's climates, I should mention that the smoke-caused decrease in temperatures would most likely be offset by the carbon dioxide-caused greenhouse effect.

In any case, if we don't destroy ourselves first, we are eventually going to run out of fossil fuels—a prospect surely not many generations away. Then, presumably, we shall turn to atomic energy (although, like the fossil fuels, it represents a nonrenewable resource; one would think that its present custodians could find better things to do with it than create explosions). And then we will face a different breed of environmental pollution.

I am aware that reactors to produce electricity are already in use or under development, but I am apprehensive of what I know of the present generation of reactors and those proposed for the future.

The uranium fuel used in present reactors has to be reprocessed periodically to keep the chain reaction going. The reprocessing yields long-lived and biologically hazardous isotopes such as ^{90}Strontium and ^{137}Cesium that should be stored where they cannot contaminate the environment for at least 1,000 years; yet a goodly number of the storage tanks employed for this purpose are already leaking. At least these products of reprocessing can be chemically trapped and stored; another product, ^{85}Krypton, cannot be so trapped—it is sent into the atmosphere to add to the radiation exposure of the earth's biota, including man, and I don't think that anyone knows a practicable way to prevent this.

To soothe our concern about the pollution of the environment involved in fission reactors, we are glibly offered the prospect of "clean" fusion bombs and reactors. They do not require reprocessing and thus would not produce the Strontium, Cesium and Krypton isotopes. But to the best of my knowledge, no one knows how this generation of reactors is to be built. And even if development is successful, fusion reactors will produce new contaminants. One such is tritium (^{3}Hydrogen) which would become a constituent of water—and that water with its long-lived radioactivity would contaminate all environments and living things. The danger of tritium was underlined in an official publication of the Atomic Energy Commission in which it was suggested that for certain mining operations it might be better to use fission (i.e. "dirty") devices rather than fusion (i.e. "clean") devices "to avoid ground water contamination."

A prime example of what irresponsible use of atomic power could bring about is provided by the proposal to use nuclear explosives to dig a sea-level canal across central America. The argument in its favor is that it is evidently the most economical way to accomplish the task. Yet consider the effects upon our environment. If 179 megatons of nuclear charges will do the job, as has been estimated by the Corps of Engineers which apparently wants to do it, and if the fission explosions take place in average materials of the earth's crust, enough ^{137}Cesium would be produced to give every person on earth a radioactive dosage 26.5 times the permissible exposure level. Cesium behaves as a gas in such a cratering explosion, and prevailing winds in the region are from east to west, so the Pacific area would presumably be contaminated first. And Cesium moves right up through biological food chains, so we could anticipate its rapid dissemination among living things.

The sea-level canal proposal also poses other dangers, whether or not atomic explosives are used. In that latitude, the Pacific Ocean stands higher than the Atlantic by a disputed amount I believe to average six feet. The tides are out of phase on the two sides of the Isthmus of Panama, so the maximum difference in level can be as great as eighteen feet; and the Pacific has much colder water than the Atlantic.

Just what would happen to climates or to sea food industries in the Caribbean if a new canal moved a mass of cold Pacific water in there is uncertain; but I have heard suggestions that it might create a new hurricane center, or even bring about diversion of the Gulf Stream with a drastic effect on the climates of all regions bordering the North Atlantic. We know that the sea-level Suez Canal permitted the exchange of many marine species between the Red Sea and the Mediterranean. We know that the Welland Canal let sea lampreys and alewives enter the upper Great Lakes with disastrous effects on fisheries and, more recently, on bathing beaches. We just don't know what disruptions of this sort a sea-level canal in the Isthmus might cause.

So much of the danger to man is summed up in that simple phrase, "We don't know." For example, consider the nitrogen cycle, which provides that element all organisms require for the building of proteins. Nitrogen is released into the atmosphere, along with ammonia, as a gas when plants and animals decay; live plants use both elements to build their proteins, but they cannot use nitrogen in gaseous form—that task is accomplished by certain bacteria and primitive algae in the soil and the roots of some plants. Animals build their proteins from the constituents of plant proteins. As in the case of oxygen, the rates of use and return of nitrogen have reached a balance so that the percentage of nitrogen in the atmosphere remains constant.

If any one of these numerous steps in the nitrogen cycle were to be disrupted, disaster would ensure for life on earth. Depending upon which step broke down, the nitrogen in the atmosphere might disappear, it might be replaced by poisonous ammonia or it might remain unused in the atmosphere because the plants could not absorb it in gaseous form.

Are any of these possibilities at hand? Has man's interference with natural processes begun to have a serious effect on the nitrogen cycle? The point is, we don't know—and we should, before we do too much more interfering.

We are dumping vast quantities of pollutants into the oceans. According to one estimate by the United States Food and Drug Administration, these include a half-million substances; many are of recent origin, including biologically active materials such as pesticides, radioisotopes, and detergents to which the ocean's living forms have never before had to try to adapt. No more than a minute fraction of these substances or the combinations of them have been tested for toxicity to life—to the diatoms, the microscopic marine plants that produce most of the earth's oxygen, or to the bacteria and microorganisms involved in the nitrogen cycle.

If the tanker Torrey Canyon had been carrying a concentrated herbicide instead of petroleum, could photosynthesis in the North Sea have been stopped? Again, we don't know, but Berkner is said to have believed that a very few instances of herbicide pollution occurring in certain areas of the ocean that are high in photosynthetic activity might cause the ultimate disaster.

Man has developed ingenious products and devices to bring about short-range benefits. He is constantly devising grandiose schemes to achieve immediate ends—the UNESCO plan of twenty years ago, for example, to "develop" the Amazon basin, which I am happy to say has since been judged impracticable. Surely man's influence on his earth is now so predominant, so all-pervasive, that he must stop trusting to luck that his products and schemes will not upset any of the indispensible biogeochemical cycles.

The interference with these delicately balanced cycles is not, however, the only instance of man's misuse of his natural heritage. He has also succeeded in rendering useless huge tracts of the earth's arable land.

We hear a lot today about "underdeveloped" and "developing" nations, but many of them might more accurately be called "overdeveloped." The valleys of the Tigris and Euphrates rivers, for example, were supporting the Sumerian civilization in 3500 B.C.E. By the year 2000 B.C.E., a great irrigation complex based on these rivers had turned the area into the granary of the great Babylonian Empire (Pliny says that the Babylonians harvested two crops of grain each year and grazed sheep on the land between crops). But today less than twenty per cent of the land in Iraq is cultivated; more than half of the nation's income is from oil. The landscape is dotted with mounds, the remains of forgotten towns; the ancient irrigation works are filled with silt, the end product of soil erosion, and the ancient seaport of Ur is now 150 miles from the sea, its buildings buried under as much as 35 feet of silt.

The valley of the Nile was another cradle of civilization. Every year the river overflowed its banks at a predictable time, bringing water to the land and depositing a layer of soil rich in mineral nutrients for plants. Crops could be grown for seven months of the year.

Extensive irrigation systems were established in the valley before 2000 B.C.E. The land was the granary of the Roman Empire, and continued to flourish for another 2,000 years. But in modern times, economic considerations have inspired governments to divert the land from food to cash crops such as cotton in spite of the desperate need for more foodstuffs to feed a growing population. In 1902 a dam was built at Aswan to prevent the spring flood and to make possible year-round irrigation, and since then the soils have deteriorated through salinization and productivity in the valley has decreased.

Salinization is a typical phenomenon of arid regions where evaporation is greater than precipitation. Rainwater soaks into the earth, dissolving salts as it goes; when the sun appears, evaporation at the earth's surface draws this salty water upward by capillary action; and when this water in turn evaporates, it leaves a deposit of salts on the surface. The essential condition for salinization to take place is a net upward movement of water.

Irrigation in arid areas, though it may have short-range benefits, can also be fraught with long-range dangers. The large quantities of water used in irrigation are added to the water table, raising it to the level of the irrigation ditch bottom—that is to say, the ground below that point is saturated with water. Otherwise, of course, the water in the ditches would soak right down into the earth immediately below, rather than spreading outward to nourish land on either side. But this results in a sideward and then upward movement of the irrigation water toward the surface. And when the salt-laden water reaches the surface and evaporates, salinization occurs. Unless great care is taken, irrigation can thus eventually ruin land—and it has often done so. The new Aswan high dam is designed to bring another million acres of land under irrigation, and it may well prove to be the ultimate disaster for Egypt.

Such sorry stories could be told for country after country. The glories of ancient Mali and Ghana in West Africa were legends in medieval Europe. Ancient Greece had forested hills, ample water, and productive soil. In the land that once exported the cedars of Lebanon to Egypt, the erosion-proof old Roman roads now stand several feet above a rock desert. In China and India ancient irrigation systems stand abandoned and filled with silt.

When the British assumed the rule of India two centuries ago, the population was about 60 million. Today it is about 500 million, and most of the nation's land problems have been created in the past century by deforestation and plowing and the resulting erosion and siltation, all stemming from efforts to support this fantastic population growth.

Overdevelopment is not confined to the Old World. Archeologists have long wondered how the Mayas managed to support what was obviously a high civilization on the now unproductive soils of Guatemala and Yucatan. Evidently they exploited their land as intensively as possible, until its fertility was exhausted and their civilization collapsed.

As recently as the present decade, aerial reconnaissance has revealed ancient ridged fields on flood plains, the remnants of a specialized system of agriculture that is believed to have transformed much of South America. This same system of constructing ridges on seasonal swamps—to raise some of the land above the flood level for planting and to capture some of the flood water—has been observed in Tanzania in Africa. The South American ridges occur in areas now considered unfit for agriculture; and though any cause and effect relationship between ridges and land ruin has not been established for those areas, it has been demonstrated in Africa where the practice is known to accelerate erosion.

Even our own young country has not been immune to deterioration. We have lost many thousands of acres to erosion and gullying and many thousands more to strip mining. It has been estimated that the agricultural value of Iowa farmland, which is about as good land as we have, is declining by 1 per cent per year. In our irrigated lands of the West there is the constant danger of salinization.

We have other kinds of water problems as well. We are pumping water from wells so much faster than it can be replaced that we have drastically lowered water tables; in some coastal regions the water table has dipped below sea level, with the result that salt water is seeping into the water-bearing strata. Meanwhile, an estimated 2,000 irrigation dams in the United States have become useless impoundments of silt, sand, and gravel.

So this is the heritage of man's past—an impoverished land, a threat to the biogeochemical cycles. And what are we doing about it?

I don't want to comment on the advertising executive who asserts that billboards are "the art gallery of the public" or on the industry spokesman who says that "the ability of a river to absorb sewage is one of our great natural resources and should be utilized to the utmost." In the face of such self-serving statements, the efforts of those who try to promote conservation on aesthetic grounds seem inevitably doomed. It makes one wonder, are we selecting for genotypes who can satisfy all their aesthetic needs in our congested cities? Are the Davy Crocketts and Kit Carsons who are born today destined for asylums, jail, or suicide?

There have been suggestions made for new ways to supplement the world's food production. We hear talk of farming the ocean bottoms, for example. And there are efforts to use bacteria, fungi, or yeasts to convert petroleum directly into food for man. This is superficially attractive because it appears to be more efficient than first feeding the petroleum to a refinery and then the gasoline to tractors and other machines which eventually deliver food to us. But it is a melancholy fact that the metabolism of bacteria, fungi, and yeasts does not generate oxygen—as do the old-fashioned green plants.

What alarms me most is that only infrequently, and usually in obscure places, does one come across articles by authors who recognize that no matter what we do it is impossible to provide enough food for a world population that increases at a compound interest rate of 1.7 per cent a year. Thus, there appears to be no way for us to escape our dependence on green plants; and even with them, there is no way for us to survive except to halt population growth completely or even to undergo a period of population decrease if, as I anticipate, definitive studies show our population to be already beyond what the earth can support on a continuous basis. Just as we must control our interference with the chemical cycles that provide the atmosphere with its oxygen, carbon, and nitrogen, so must we control our birth rate.

In order to accomplish this end, natural scientists, social scientists, and political leaders will have to learn to overcome that failure of communication which I referred to earlier. And all three will have to learn to communicate with the general public. This is a large order, but I have found in recent years that intercommunication is possible between ecologists and social scientists who are concerned with population problems.

For example, as a natural scientist, it would not occur to me that in many cultures it is important to save face and prove virility by producing a child as soon after marriage as possible. In these cultures, population planners must evidently aim at delaying the age of marriage or spreading the production of children after the first. And after it has been pointed out to me, I can easily see that a tradition to produce many children would develop under social conditions where few children survive to reach maturity and families wish to assure they will have descendants.

In a Moslem country like Pakistan, where women will not allow themselves to be examined by a male physician, birth control by such measures as the intra-uterine device (IUD) is impracticable, and it is difficult to convey a monthly schedule of pill-taking to the poorly educated. However, just as the reproductive cycles of cattle can be synchronized by hormone treatments so that many cows can undergo simultaneous artificial insemination, so the menstrual cycles of populations of women can be synchronized. Then the instructions for contraception can take such a simple form as: "Take a pill every night the moon shines." But in a country like Puerto Rico the efforts of an aroused clergy to instill guilt feelings about the decision a woman must make each day can render the pill ineffective. Here, the IUD, which requires only one decision, provides an answer.

In any case, there is ample evidence that people the world over want fertility control. Voluntary sterilization is popular in India, Japan, and Latin America. In

Japan and Western European countries that have made legal abortion available upon request the birth rates have fallen dramatically. With such recent techniques as the pill and the IUD, and the impending availability of antimeiotic drugs which inhibit sperm production in the male, and anti-implantation drugs which can prevent pregnancy when taken as long as three days after exposure, practicable fertility control is at last available.

Kingsley Davis, a population expert at the University of California at Berkeley, has recently expressed skepticism about schemes for family planning on the grounds that they do not actually represent population policy but merely permit couples to determine their family size voluntarily. This is certainly true, but the evidence is overwhelming that a great many of the children born into the world today are unwanted. I think we must start by preventing these unwanted births and then take stock of what additional measures, such as negative family allowances, may be called for.

Japan has already shown that a determined people can in one generation bring the problem of excess population growth under control. The Soviet Union seems finally to have abandoned the dogma that overpopulation problems are by-products of capitalism and couldn't exist in a socialistic country. So a beginning has been made. It now becomes more urgent that social and natural scientists get together and try to decide what an optimum size for the human population of the earth would be.

I shall try to end on a note of optimism. We have seen the start of efforts at meaningful birth control. A five-year study, known as the International Biological Program, is investigating the effects that man is having on the environment. If the world's best minds can at last come to grips with the population problem and effect its control, and if this can be achieved before some miscalculation, or noncalculation, sends the earth environment into an irreversible decline, then there indeed may be some hope that the world can be saved.

Where Religion
and Science
Meet

Roland B. Gittelsohn

N O EVALUATION by a clergyman of the relationship between religion and science can be worth its weight in words unless it begins with a clear identification of the perspective from which he speaks. This is true because we live at a time of incredibly swift and profound ideological transition. Such a time is characterized necessarily by semantic confusion. Words which once had precise meanings become annoyingly confused. For some they retain their old meanings, while for others they have already acquired colorations and shadings that are quite new.

This is what has happened in the last two generations to the word "religion." It is used now to designate men and positions which are seen, upon careful analysis, to share little beyond the label itself. Let me be specific. The Bible Belt Christian fundamentalist of the deep South is called "religious," as I am. A scientifically oriented agnostic like Julian Huxley is generally considered to be nonreligious, as I am not. Yet if one were painstakingly to spell out specific attitudes toward the universe and human life, he would discover that I share more with Huxley than with the southern evangelist. My attitudes toward science must therefore be expected to differ considerably from those of the Orthodox Protestant or the Roman Catholic or, for that matter, even of some among my fellow Jews. This despite the fact that with a certain measure of validity all of us are at this juncture in time considered to be religious. Where, then, do I stand as I propose to ponder science?

I am a naturalistic, humanistic theist. Naturalistic, because I believe that God inheres within nature rather than operating upon it from outside itself. Humanistic, because I am convinced that the loftiest human values we have been able to conceive represent the closest our finite minds can come as yet to comprehending the Infinite. Theist, because I am persuaded that our spiritual propensities and capacities are reflections of something very close to the crux of Ultimate Reality. Each of the terms now invites further elaboration.

196

My identification as a naturalist does not automatically make me a pantheist. I do not equate God with nature or assert that God is nature; rather that God permeates and infuses nature. God is to nature, as it were, what electric current is to a motor: the Creative Energy which transforms into a vital process what would otherwise either not exist at all or at best be lifeless and inert.

I do not believe in what most people mean by miracles. For me, one of the most convincing kinds of evidence that God exists is to be found precisely in the fact that there are no exceptions to the laws of nature. It will be a very long time, if ever, before I shall be able to know all the laws of nature, but I know enough already to be confident that they can be abrogated by neither man nor God. Indeed, if they could be suspended or interrupted by either, I should then have to become an atheist. For then the very principle and power of purposive development which I call God would have vanished from the universe.

My humanistic theism means that I cannot see our unique ability as human beings to create and appreciate truth, goodness, and beauty as divorced from the rest of reality. I believe this dimension of man's experience has evolved in response to the nature and structure of the universe no less than has his hand or brain. There must, therefore, be something in the universe itself which is closely akin to this aspect of man's life. Which is to say, there must be God.

Here, then, is the religious position and perspective from which I ponder science. From this point of departure, what do I find?

First, an alarming (and I fear growing) tendency to resolve the erstwhile conflict between religion and science through by-pass rather than confrontation. There was a time when chiefly religionists were heard to say that religion and science do not conflict because they do not really meet, that they occupy altogether different and unrelated areas of man's concern, that science is preoccupied with facts and religion with values, that what we *believe* as matters of faith cannot be affected one way or another by what we *know* through empirical research. Now—amazingly and regrettably—a similar chant has been taken up by some among our scientists.

Typical of this view are statements by two eminent psychiatrists. Dr. Harry Solomon, commissioner of Mental Health for the Commonwealth of Massachusetts, has written the following in private correspondence with the author: "I see no reason why one cannot have deep faith on one hand and be deeply involved in scientific study on the other hand without worrying whether one negates the other." The late Dr. Gregory Zilboorg was even more explicit: "Scientific knowledge is essentially different from religious knowledge, and it is impossible to measure one by the other; . . . religious beliefs need no scientific proof, nor are they made less valid by scientific refutations." He achieves the logical climax and consequence of this view by quoting W. T. Stace to the effect that "science is irrelevant to religion."

I must protest with utmost vehemence and vigor this attempt to reconcile religion and science by detour or avoidance. It is not true that religion and science yield two different and unrelated kinds of knowledge. Knowledge is knowledge, whatever its source. There is indeed a difference between knowledge and faith, both of which play significant roles in science as well as religion, but not between one kind of knowledge and another. There is, to be sure, more than one source of knowledge, but not more than one kind. What we know, we know.

I reject no less perfervidly the implied cleaving of man or reality into neat and unrelated compartments, amounting almost to a kind of philosophic schizophrenia. If science and religion have conspired to teach me any one abiding truth, it is that man is one, the universe is one, and man and the universe together are one. This is the central meaning of science and the core of Judaism's watchword: "Hear O Israel, the Lord our God, the Lord is One."

This means that man cannot be divided into a believing creature versus a thinking creature, that his faith and reason, while not identical, are yet indivisible. What he knows must be the basis of what he believes. What he believes must be consonant with what he knows. I have elsewhere expressed myself on this point as follows: "Of course we need faith to carry us beyond the bounds of reason. But that faith must be built on a foundation of reason, must be consistent with the reasonable and the known, not contradictory to them."

To juxtapose mind and faith, human investigation and divine revelation, as if they were irreconcilable opposites, is for me utterly fallacious. Man's intelligence, his conscience, and his sensitivity are the very best instruments he possesses to ascertain the Divine. Revelation is not the miraculous one-way intrusion of the divine into the mundane. It is rather the result of progressive interaction between man and God. Whenever or wherever a human being reaches out to grasp a truth that has never been comprehended before, or to create or appreciate a higher dimension of beauty, or to achieve a loftier level of ethical conduct, there and then God has revealed himself to man again. Divine revelation is just as apt to take place in a laboratory or studio as it is in a pulpit.

I like particularly the way Dr. Meier Ben-Horin expresses this concept of revelation, with its creative implications for the relationship between religion and science. Skillfully playing upon the words of the biblical assertion, "Near is the Lord unto all who call Him, unto all who call Him in truth," he interprets this to mean: "God is called *in truth*. To find a new truth is to come nearer to His nearness."

All of which adds up to my very firm conviction that the only valid ground for a true synthesis of religion and science is to view them as coordinated, complementary, and simultaneous approaches to man as a whole and life as a whole. They must not only coexist; they must reinforce and refine each other.

But do they in fact do this? To a greater degree than small minds on either side of the equation have been able to perceive, yes. It is time for both religionists and scientists to realize the extent to which their most significant insights coincide.

198

True, many of the incidental superstitions by which the essential message of religion has in the course of time become encrusted have been discredited. So have some of the earlier dogmatisms of science, or, perhaps it would be more accurate to say, of some scientists. But in remarkable respects the newer findings and conclusions of science confirm rather than threaten the earlier intuitions of religion. Perhaps this can best be understood through three stages of exposition.

First, science reveals a universe of ineffably wondrous order. This has always been a prime postulate of high religion. The fact that science speaks more frequently today in the vocabulary of statistical probability than in that of law must not be allowed to obscure the truth involved: that our universe is not a haphazard or capricious puzzle; that, despite the many mysteries which will long—perhaps forever—remain, there are reliable, predictable patterns; and in proportion to our success in discovering these patterns we can increasingly understand the universe and manipulate it to our enormous benefit. Every scientific experiment is predicated on the premise that this is so.

Second, science has emerged from the stark mechanism and materialism by which so much of its infancy was marked. It is much more inclined now to interpret reality in terms of energy and process than of matter, even speculating at times on whether they may not be identical. In so far as human life is concerned, it recognizes the intimate interrelationship and mutual sway of mind and body over each other. Significant numbers of scientists have at least tentatively voiced the hypothesis that primal energy evolved into matter, then the inorganic into the organic, the unconscious into the conscious, the amoral into the moral, the physical into the extraphysical or spiritual—with each successive stage at least potentially present in its predecessor. This is very close indeed to my understanding of religion.

Third, science has provided the strongest bulwark for a point of view which was adumbrated earlier and to which we must now return, namely, that man in all his aspects and proclivities is an integral part of his universe. He is made of the same stuff as the universe. He could perhaps be perceptively defined as the stuff of the universe become conscious of itself. On the level of the physical, science and religion would agree that this is so. What religion would hasten to add is that no less is true of the extraphysical or spiritual in man. It too must have its counterpart in the larger cosmos.

Thomas Huxley seemed almost to be groping for this very truth a century ago when he wrote: ". . . man, physical, intellectual, and moral, is as much a part of nature, as purely a part of the cosmic process, as the humblest weed."

His grandson, Julian, consummated what the elder Huxley had only implied: "The evolutionary point of view . . . establishes the reassuring fact that our human ethics have their roots deep in the nonhuman universe, that our moral principles are not just a whistling in the dark, not just the *ipse dixit* of an isolated humanity, but are by the nature of things related to the rest of reality."

Here we come close to the most exciting confluence of religion and science. To my knowledge, no one has expressed it more eloquently or incisively than the Canadian zoologist, Dr. Norman J. Berrill: ". . . our knowledge of the universe through our senses and our knowledge of the universe through our own inward nature shows that it is orderly, moral, and beautiful, that it is akin to intelligence, that love and hope belong in it as fully as light itself, and that the power and will of the human mind is but a symptom of reality; that we, when we are most human, most rational, most aware of love and beauty, reflect and represent the spirit of the universe."

This brings us to a question which seems to bother many of my colleagues in the clergy, both Christian and Jewish. Does the foregoing mean that religion is dependent upon science for validation, that we can accept on faith only that which science shows demonstrably to be true? My answer is, of course, in the negative. Here is where our distinction between knowledge and faith comes again into focus. It does not require faith to accept that which has already been proven as fact. Religion will always, must always, go beyond science in postulating hypotheses about life, especially about the spiritual dimensions of life, hypotheses and convictions which science may never be able to prove or disprove.

Science must be depended upon, not necessarily in every instance to validate, but when necessary to veto the assertions of religion when they uphold on faith that which has already been proven impossible in fact. Specifically, science possesses both the right and the duty to deny, with reference to the biblical account of creation, that this earth with all its precious cargo could possibly have been created in six days or that one pair of fully developed human beings named Adam and Eve ever appeared on our planet at a precise moment of time as the progenitors of the whole human race. Religion, in turn, has both right and duty to proclaim that life developed gradually on the earth—and perhaps elsewhere, too—as an expression of a massive Cosmic Energy or Urge which has been designated through the ages as God. Between religion thus conceived and science thus understood there can be only collaboration, not conflict.

What I am struggling to express here comes close, I suspect, to Erich Fromm's distinction between rational faith and irrational faith. By the latter he means the blind acceptance of any "truth" simply on the authority of some individual or group that has proclaimed it. By the former he means the acceptance of a given doctrine as "true" because my own reason and experience, together with those of any number of authorities, convince me that it is valid.

In this light the obligations and responsibilities of both religion and science become clear. Science must guard against the dogmatic assumption that only that which can be demonstrated in a laboratory can be true. Religion must refrain from arrogantly disputing with science its discoveries of fact. Both must understand that absolute knowledge is possessed by neither, that everything we think we know—whether it be religious doctrine or scientific data—has been filtered through finite and fallible human intelligence. No individual, discipline, or sect has a monopoly on such intelligence. All that any of us has a decent right to claim is that he is doing the very best he can, at this moment in history and consistent with his own limitations both of knowledge and of faith, to understand life and to live it more decently.

May I be forgiven a brief word of *ex parte* pleading at this point? Even as science must very properly appeal for religion to keep abreast of man's expanding knowledge, so that it will never claim as true on faith that which has already been discovered to be false in fact, so religion should petition science to remain aware of significant changes within the household of theology. Too often the spokesmen of science act as if nothing had happened to religion since 1800. Instead of setting up straw men in the likeness of medieval faith and exulting over the ease with which they can swiftly be demolished, let science, consistent with its own essential nature, take pains to acquaint itself with the newer voices of religion, voices which have been more than a little responsive to the importunings of science itself.

At this fateful juncture in time, mature religion and mature science can ill afford to continue a quarrel which has long since lost its meaning. It will require the most precious talents of both if either is to survive.

As I wrote in *Man's Best Hope,* "Science helps us take our bearings in the journey through evolution. Science and religion together enable us to project the probable future. We see ourselves not as the end-result of evolution but as a way-station en route to something incomparably more wonderful.

"Thus, through science and religion together, we arrive at an understanding of meaning in life. We become aware not only of the present as it has evolved from the past, but also of our human responsibility to the future. Neither science nor religion alone can give us this. Only religion modified by the insights of science and science tempered by devotion to spiritual values can save us or make us worth saving."

Science vs. Religion in the 20th Century

Harry Posner

I. GENERAL STATEMENT OF THE PROBLEM

"I grow aware
Of an appalling mystery . . . We, this throng
Of midgets, playing, tense and still,
Are sailing on a midget ball of dust . . .
What does it mean? Oh, God, what can it mean?"

—Alfred Noyes

This outburst of the poet is a spontaneous expression of awe and bafflement which fill the hearts and minds of all thinking men. It is a conflict between man's established faith and the revelations disclosed by science. Let us review the situation.

For many years the principle of *mutability* and *evolution* as applied to the whole of the universe has been the subject of prolonged and bitter controversy between the men of science and the men of the cloth. During the nineteenth century, science made such phenomenal strides that it emboldened its devotees to make the claim that they had finally penetrated the innermost secrets of creation. Henceforth, they loudly proclaimed, the tenets of organized religion are to be completely disregarded in the formulation of theories pertaining to the origin and the development of the cosmos.

And what of the Church? Its devotees have been equally adamant in their insistence that the laws of nature are immutable, that is, they are not subject to change and evolution, and must follow the dictates of God as prescribed by the Church. Any one who is beset by doubts or misgivings concerning the views of the Church on this subject is guilty of heresy.

Changes in Both Scientists and Clergy

A complete stalemate ensued which appeared to be unbreakable. However, starting with the turn of this century, slowly but inexorably a significant change began to take place in the points of view of both the scientists and the clergy. The agnostic tendencies of the former have, over the years, given way in the face of the ever-mounting difficulties and complexities they have been and still are encountering in their search for the secrets of nature, either in the infinitely vast reaches of the heavens or in the infinitely small recesses of the atom. They have, instead, become aware of an all-pervading manifestation of a cosmic intelligence which transcends all human understanding.

The Church, too, has undergone a drastic change of orientation in its views. The cumulative impact of the discoveries made by the sciences of astronomy, physics, chemistry, and biology has brought to it an awareness of the principle of *mutability* and *evolution* throughout the universe which can no longer be denied. It has also become conscious of the fact that the advances of science have imparted a far deeper meaning to "the Power, the Wisdom, and the Glory" of God expressed in the Lord's prayer than did the canons of established religion.

This rapprochement is eloquently expressed by Dr. Robert A. Millikan, Nobel Prize winner in 1923 for isolating the electron, when he said: "The spirit of religion and the spirit of science are going to join hands because the leaders of both religion and science are coming increasingly to see life as a whole instead of from the pathetically narrow and unscientific point of view from which some in both fields have in the past looked upon it."[1]

Two Supplementary Roles

Dr. Millikan's book, *Science and Life*, contains a statement on the relations of science and religion issued by a group of prominent scientists, religious leaders, and men of affairs, and signed by 15 great scientists, 16 religious leaders and 14 outstanding men of affairs. It was issued in June, 1923, and is worded as follows:

"We, the undersigned, deeply regret that in recent controversies there has been a tendency to present science and religion as irreconcilable and antagonistic domains of thought, for in fact they meet distinct human needs and, in rounding out of human life, they supplement rather than displace or oppose each other.

"The purpose of science is to develop without prejudice or preconception of any kind a knowledge of facts, the laws and the processes of nature. The even more important task of religion, on the other hand, is to develop the consciences, the ideals, and the aspirations of mankind. Each of these two activities represents a deep and vital function of the soul of man, and both are necessary for the life, the progress, and the happiness of the human race.

1. *Science and Religion*, by Robert Andrews Millikan, Pilgrim Press, Boston, Chicago, 1924.

"It is a sublime conception of God which is furnished by science, and one wholly consonant with the highest ideals of religion, when it represents Him (God) as revealing himself through countless ages in the development of the earth as an abode for man and in the age-long inbreathing of life into its constituent matter, culminating in man with his spiritual nature and all his God-like powers."

This was the situation at the end of the first quarter of this century. What is the situation now, four and a half decades since this resolution was penned? Has the spirit of rapprochement between science and religion progressed or retrogressed? It has definitely progressed. This is clearly evident from the writings of H. T. Stetson (1930), Sir James Jeans (1931), Albert Einstein (1950), Pope Pius XII (1951), Fred Hoyle (1956), Paul Tillich (1957), Harlow Shapley (1958), Martin Cyril D'Arcy (1960), and Mordecai M. Kaplan (1966).

The Proper Story of Mankind . . .

It is of particular interest to note that in recent years a group of some two hundred researchers, consisting of scientists from several disciplines and from a score of universities and colleges, clergy from various denominations, and laymen, have come together to inquire, discuss, and ponder on the nature of man, his goals and the types and justification of his various beliefs. These week-long summer meetings have been and still are being held periodically at Star Island off the coast of Maine and New Hampshire.

The scope of their investigations was described by one of the participants as follows: "We are citizens of the universe. The proper study of mankind should therefore not be only man himself . . . but should be the universe—its contents, its mechanics, the atoms in time and space, and the molecules in organisms; it should be the electrochemical operators that we call nerves, brain, and mind, and the socializing impulse that puts simple atoms into molecular complexes; that puts bees and ants into colonies, and man into civilizations. These paths to understanding should all be followed for the proper study of mankind."[2]

Harlow Shapley selected eighteen essays contributed by some of the participants in writing, and published them in his book *Science Ponders Religion*.

II. THE RELIGIONISTS SPEAK

To present the point of view of the religionists, I have chosen the following: Pope Pius XII, Paul Tillich, Martin Cyril D'Arcy, Mordecai M. Kaplan.

Pope Pius XII

In his address to the Vatican Academy of Science in September 1951, the Pope stated:

---

2. *Science Ponders Religion*, by Harlow Shapley, Appleton-Century-Crofts, Inc., New York, 1962.

"At first sight it is rightly a source of wonderment to recognize how the knowledge of the fact of mutability has gained ever greater ground, both in the macrocosm (realm of the stars) and in the microcosm (realm of the atom), according as science has made progress, as though confirming with new proof the theory of Heraclitus. 'Panta Rhei—everything is in flux.' As is known, our own everyday experience brings to light an immense number of transformations in the world around us, both near and far away . . . Going still further, natural science has made known that the chemicophysical mutability is not, as the ancients thought, restricted to terrestrial bodies, but even extends to all the bodies of our solar system and of the great universe, which the telescope and still more, the microscope, have demonstrated to be composed of the same kind of atoms. . . .

"The pertinent facts of the natural sciences, to which we have referred, as awaiting still further research and confirmation, and the theories founded on them are in need of further development and proof before they can provide a sure foundation for arguments which of themselves are outside the proper sphere of the natural sciences. This notwithstanding, it is worthy of note that modern scholars in these fields regard the idea of the creation of the universe as entirely compatible with their scientific conceptions and that they are even led spontaneously to this conclusion by their scientific research. Just a few decades ago, any such 'hypothesis' was rejected as entirely irreconcilable with the present state of science."[3]

The Pope refers to the intransigence of the scientists. What about the clerics? Shades of Galileo and Giordano Bruno! The former was excommunicated from the Church and the latter was burned at the stake for merely holding the view that the earth was not the center of the universe and that the sun, the moon, and the stars were not hung out in the heavens for the sole benefit and amusement of mortal man. This occurred only 300 years ago. We have gone a long way since then. Yes, indeed! It was a hard road the Church had to travel from Pope Urban VIII to Pope Pius XII. Be it said to its everlasting credit that the Church traveled it nevertheless.

Martin Cyril D'Arcy

Dr. D'Arcy, in his paper appearing in the series compiled under the heading "Adventures of the Mind," carries the thesis of evolution to a very intriguing conclusion. I am quoting an excerpt from this paper, as follows:

"To judge from the religious ideas now current, and the boldness of some of them, a new synthesis, or an old synthesis with a new look is being premeditated. What else can explain the fearless effort of the late Père Teilhard de Chardin to rope together evolution and the Christian religion? Other writers have offered ingenious solutions of the fall of man, and of nature too, in terms of evolution,

---

3. *Of Stars and Men,* by Harlow Shapley, Beacon Press, Boston, 1958.

but Père Teilhard goes much further and argues that man is still developing and, under the direction of Christianity, is evolving into a higher species.

"As a scientist of high repute, one of those responsible for the verdict on the Peking man, and, at the same time a distinguished priest of the Catholic Church, Père Teilhard was in the happy position of being able to speak with some authority as a scientist and as a Christian. He was convinced that the secret of the universe lay in evolution, which he regarded as 'regular, continuous, and total.' There is, he reasoned, a continuous, upward process from matter to the organic, and from the organic to Homo sapiens and still higher. Man is the end product, so far, of nature, and able, therefore, to reflect and discover the truth about nature and himself. Mankind is one, but is not invariant. Owing to the power of reflection, man is in the process of evolving into a new super organism or species, which will individually and collectively mirror reality in its mind. It will be co-conscious and one in truth and affection. To use Père Teilhard's own words, 'There will be only one science, one ethic, and one passion, that is to say, one mystique!' The present time may seem to be a melting pot; but 'man is in process of reemerging . . . as the head of nature. The reason is that by being in this way cast into the general current of a convergent cosmogenesis he acquires the power and the quality of forming, in the very heart of time and space, a central and singular gathering point of the whole stuff of the universe.' This cosmos of affection and thought must in turn be centered around One, who is the Word by and in whom all things were made and have their meaning.

"That scientists of many countries should have willingly supported the publication of Père Teilhard's ideas shows the general respect for these ideas. Few probably would entirely concur with them. The Catholic theologians, on their side, are also critical; not so much, I think, because of any distaste for the theme as for the defects in the argument. I believe that more work has still to be done by both philosophers and scientists before evolution can pass from a working hypothesis to a general philosophical theory."[4]

This is a daring view of the ultimate end of evolution and, coming from a prominent clergyman, it almost takes one's breath away. But, then, it must be remembered that the famous theory of the "Expanding Universe" was first put forward by another clergyman, Abbé Lemaître, a Belgian. I must emphasize, however, that Dr. D'Arcy, Abbé Lemaître, and Pope Pius XII held, of course, to the precept of the supremacy of God.

Paul Tillich

Dr. Tillich draws a distinct line between faith as dictated by religion and science as dictated by knowledge. The following is an excerpt from his book, *The Dynamics of Faith:*

---

4. *Adventures of the Mind,* First Series, Alfred A. Knopf, New York, 1962.

206

"Faith does not affirm or deny what belongs to the prescientific or scientific knowledge of our world, whether we know it by direct experience or through the experience of others. The knowledge of our world (including ourselves as a part of the world) is a matter of inquiry by ourselves or by those in whom we trust. It is not a matter of faith. The dimension of faith is not the dimension of science, history, or psychology. The acceptance of a probable hypothesis in these realms is not faith, but preliminary belief to be tested by scholarly methods and to be changed by every new discovery. Almost all the struggles between faith and knowledge are rooted in the wrong understanding of faith as a type of knowledge which has a low degree of evidence but is supported by religious authority. It is, however, not only confusion of faith with knowledge that is responsible for the world historical conflict between them, it is also the fact that matters of faith lie hidden behind an assumedly scientific method. Whenever this happens, faith stands against faith and not against knowledge.

"The difference between faith and knowledge is also visible in the kind of certitude each gives. There are two types of knowledge which are based on complete evidence and give complete certitude. The one is immediate evidence of sense perception . . . the other complete evidence is that of the logical and mathematical rules which are presupposed even if their formulation admits different and sometimes conflicting methods. One cannot discuss logic without presupposing those implicit rules which make the discussion meaningful.

"Knowledge of reality has never the certitude of complete evidence. The process of knowing is infinite. It never comes to an end except in a state of knowledge of the whole. But such knowledge transcends infinitely every finite mind and can be ascribed only to God. . . ."[5]

Dr. Tillich has no quarrel with science, or the results of its research, but he maintains that you just can't rationalize faith, or "prove" the existence of God. You accept God as the Creator of the universe, because otherwise the universe wouldn't be here, nor man either.

Mordecai M. Kaplan

From Dr. Kaplan, who has created a revolution in the conventional conception of Judaism and who is the founder of the Reconstructionist movement in the Jewish religious community, I have taken the following declarations:

"By now we are beginning to realize that godhood is the process within and without mankind that makes for its salvation. By the same token that we dread insanity and repel moral disintegration within ourself, we dread the thought of a world governed by mere chance, and repel the assumption of a meaningless and godless universe.

---

5. *Dynamics of Faith,* by Paul Tillich, Harper & Brothers Publishers, New York, 1957.

"Many people who find the traditional concept of God as a 'worker of miracles' untenable become atheists. They cannot understand a concept of God in which He is regarded as working in and through nature. They say you have no right to change the meaning of the term 'god.'

"One wonders what they would say about the term 'atom.' It used to be considered the smallest possible particle of matter. The very term means, from the Greek, an uncuttable portion of matter. Now that we can split an atom, shall we give up the term?

"Why not extend the same privilege of redefinition to the term 'god'? Henceforth it should mean the Power that makes for the realization of human destiny.

"God-impulse in us is not fear but hope, not helplessness but self-help, not despondency but courage, not obfuscation of the mind but the light of reason, not belittlement of what man is but exaltation of what he might be. . . .

"The trouble with present-day religious education is that it fails to teach people what they should expect of religion.

"All it teaches at present is that religion means loyalty to one's particular denomination and traditions.

"What it should teach is that religion should encourage freedom of thought, emphasize the service of man as the highest service of God, and insist on our regarding all human beings as deserving to be served.

"When the theologians gloat over the failure of 'Salvation by Science' they forget two things. First, science never promised to bring salvation: it only promised to create the *conditions* necessary to salvation, and it has kept its promise. Second, theology, ever since it has been in existence, has done nothing but promise salvation, and so far has not brought mankind even within hailing distance of it."[6]

If the statement of D'Arcy, coming from a distinguished priest of the Catholic Church, is indeed very startling, the statement made by Mordecai Kaplan, a foremost exponent of religious philosophy in the non-Orthodox Jewish religious community, sounds downright revolutionary to those who adhere to the *status quo*.

III. THE SCIENTISTS SPEAK

To present the scientific point of view I have chosen the following: Harlan T. Stetson, Sir James Jeans, Harlow Shapley, Fred Hoyle, and Albert Einstein.

As in the case with the opinions of the clergymen, I shall endeavor to present the views of the scientists by using actual quotations from their works, being careful, of course, not to use matter out of context.

---

6. *Not So Random Thoughts,* by Mordecai M. Kaplan, The Reconstructionist Press, New York, 1966.

Harlan T. Stetson

A somewhat guarded acceptance of the idea that the relentless search by science into the mysteries of creation will ultimately reveal the presence of a power and purpose which must be ascribed to an omniscient creator is expressed by astronomer Harlan T. Stetson in his book, *Man and the Stars*. I quote:

"A little while ago I stood in the museum at Cairo looking at the mummy of the supposed Pharaoh of the Exodus. Two sightseers strolled by. Glancing at the mummy one seized the occasion to remark on the absurdity of the idea of immortality.

"The dogmatic character of the assertion made me say to myself: Are you sure? Too many times have scientists been deceived by the physical appearances of things in the material universe to care to make dogmatic statements in a realm all unknown. Golden streets and tormenting fires have too long colored ideas of the persistence of life to lead to much profitable thinking of nonspecial possibilities.

"Now that physical science has made impossible a medieval cosmology, and has reduced space and time to a rather visionary framework, perhaps some future physical science shall yet evolve, that shall discover that mind after all is the one persisting reality.

"It is inevitable that the study of astronomy should make impossible the retention of certain theological conceptions of yesterday. Religious ideas must grow and expand with the maturing of the race as they do with the maturing of the individual. I hesitate to think that any vital religion shall ever ultimately suffer through the patient and persisting searchings of science in the acquisition of truth. Whatever his philosophy of life may be, every scientist is an eager explorer into fields unknown. Like Merlin, in the days of King Arthur, he pushes fearlessly on over many a rugged trail in the pursuit of each gleam that may lead to knowledge. Allured by the fascination of that which evades his grasp, he will seek, and who shall say he may not find something of even more vital significance than that yet revealed in atoms and stars?"[7]

Sir James Jeans

In his book, *The Universe Around Us*, the famed British astronomer and physicist devotes a portion of the last chapter to a discussion of the aims of the astronomer and the limitations of man's ability to solve ultimate reality. He likens the universe to a great painting and refers to its creator as the artist who is painting it. Any attempt on the part of man to identify the painter by going back in time and space is quite futile. But let Sir James tell it:

---

7. *Man and the Stars*, by Harlan Tone Stetson, McGraw-Hill Book Company, Inc., New York, 1930.

"Traveling as far back in time as we can brings us not to the creation of the picture but to its edge; the creation of the picture lies as much outside the picture as the artist is outside the canvas. On this view, discussing the creation of the universe in terms of time and space is like trying to discover the artist and the creation of the painting, by going to the edge of the picture.

"To take the simplest illustration, the Victorian scientist thought it necessary to 'explain' light as a wave motion in the mechanical ether which he was ever trying to construct out of jellies and gyroscopes; the scientist of today, fortunately for his sanity, has given up the attempt and is well satisfied if he can obtain a mathematical formula which will predict what light will do under specified conditions. It does not matter much whether the formula admits of a mechanical explanation or not, or whether such an explanation corresponds to any thinkable ultimate reality. The formulae of modern science are judged mainly, if not entirely, by their capacity for describing the phenomena of nature with simplicity, accuracy, and completeness. . . .

"This does not imply any lowering of the standards of ideals of science; it implies merely a growing conviction that the ultimate realities of the universe are at present quite beyond the reach of science, and may be—and probably are—forever beyond the comprehension of the human mind. It is a priori possible that only the artist can understand the full significance of the picture he has painted, and that this will remain forever impossible for a few specks of paint on the canvas. It is for this reason that, when we try to discuss the ultimate structure of the atom, we are driven to speak in terms of similes, metaphors, and parables. There is no need even to worry over much about apparent contradictions. The higher unity of ultimate reality must no doubt reconcile them all, although it remains to be seen whether this higher unity is within our comprehension or not. In the meantime a contradiction worries us about as much as an unexplained fact, but hardly more; it may or may not disappear in the progress of science.

"The astronomer must leave the problem at this stage. The message of astronomy is of obvious concern to philosophers, to religion, and to humanity in general, but it is not the business of the astronomer to decode it. The observing astronomer watches and records the dots and dashes of the needle which delivers the message, the theoretical astronomer translates these into words—and according as they are found to form known consistent words or not, it is known whether he has done his job well or ill—but it is for others to try to understand and explain the ultimate decoded meaning of the words he writes down."[8]

Dr. Harlow Shapley

Dr. Shapley presents a "rationalistic" interpretation of the creation without any direct reference to either "faith" or "religion." However, neither is there a denial of the existence of a creator. To quote from his book, *Of Stars and Men*:

---

8. *The Universe Around Us,* by Sir James Jeans, The Macmillan Company, New York, 1931.

"Certainly we should be humble about our trivial accomplishments in understanding the total of the external world. We know enough to get along, as do most of the other animals. We can cope with all the primitive challenges. And going farther we can construct new worlds of ideas and beauty. Our number and our work are impressive, although both number and works are limited to the surface or near the surface of one planet.

"I assume that the human mind and heart will successfully confront the hazards of mankind as they arise. This habitation on a pretty steady planet is comfortable on the average, and may get happier. . . . We have increased the length of our useful lives. We have built up ethical systems that average to bring us safety and satisfaction, but which greatly alarm and dismay us by frequent failure. We know that the rules of the stars are hard, that the flow of time is irrevocable, that death is dark and will accept no substitutes. But even so, the lights can, if we cooperate, exceed the shadows. The imagination can enter when knowledge falters. We of the higher primates have delved into the half-known cosmic facts deeply enough to recognize also the need of cosmic fancies when facts are delayed.

"It is my own belief that the central theme of biological existence is to grow in refined complexity, in durability, in adaptability. Man as half beast, half angel must comply with the biogenetic common law, but he is able to make amendments thereto.

"In scores of ways improvements are possible in the three principal fields of human activity—physical, mental, and social. In these fields we have accomplished many things since the Pliocene; we can accomplish much more. It is probable that the men of the future will overcome our shortcomings and build out of our thoughts and acts a finer mental and social structure—one that is in better keeping with nature's heavy investment in the human race.

"We no longer need appeal to anything beyond nature when we are confronted by such problems as the origin of life, or the kindling force of nucleons, or the orbits in a star cluster, or the electrochemical dynamics of a thought, or some super-entity of the material universe. We can assail all such questions *rationally.*"[9]

Fred Hoyle

Unlike his fellow scientists, Stetson, Jeans, and Shapley who treat the relationship between science and religion rather circumspectly, this celebrated British astronomer and physicist, of the younger generation, takes a more positive stand on this delicate but vital subject. In his book, *Man and Materialism*, he tackles the subject with considerable vigor. I quote:

"One of the difficult problems, perhaps the most difficult problem facing us in our effort to arrive at a rational evaluation of mankind's relationship to the universe, is the problem of 'Purpose.' Imagine that you have all the things you

---

9. *Of Stars and Men*, by Harlow Shapley.

would like, and that you have achieved all your ambitions. What then? A very dull life indeed. The word 'happiness' is one of the most difficult of all labels. Certainly happiness does not lie in a state of dreamy contemplation, it is not Nirvana. Happiness is a dynamic state of mind, associated with active fulfillment of our desires. Once fulfillment is over, happiness is lost. . . .

"By and large this matter of 'End' and 'Purpose' is most frequently satisfied in the rearing of a family; especially it is so in the case of women. But there are other 'aims' that a man or woman can have success in—a career, the solving of a scientific problem, achievement in one or the other of the arts, playing of a musical instrument, writing a book, climbing a mountain. It is the possession of one or several of these aims by the majority of individuals that keeps our modern communities in a more or less sane condition. . . .

"Where does the ultimate purpose, or aim if you like, of the human species lie? What is the point of the species reproducing itself generation by generation? Why are we journeying? It is the propounding of questions such as these, and in attempting to answer them, that religious impulses lie.

"There are no easy answers to these questions, as is clear from the multitude of contradictory religious beliefs that have been held in the world. Yet an examination of the origins of the major religions will show that in spite of the contradictions their tenets spring from a common aim: the identification of man with the universe. . . .

"It seems far more profitable to attempt to rebuild our ideas of man's relation to the universe from a new start, putting aside the older beliefs until some rational basis for discussing them has been achieved. . . .

"What then can we say of man's relation to the universe? Do we know that there is any relation at all, except that man is some curious by-product of the universe? Yes, I think we do know something rather surprising on this point" . . . and that is, "the astonishing ability of the human brain to guess the workings of the universe. It is explicable only on the basis that in some degree at least our brains mirror the universe itself. Even on the most cautious view the connection must be reckoned a most remarkable one.

"Christians say that man was created in the image of God.

"God is the universe. The Christian statement becomes very much what we have just been saying. I feel sure that many religious people would object to this association, however, but what would they offer in its place? What concept does the label 'god' stand for? Some people would seem to think of 'God' as the 'Maker' of the universe.

"This concept would place 'God' in the role of a creator who stands 'outside' the universe which He is creating analogous to the artist who stands outside the picture which he is painting." (This is precisely what Sir James Jeans has visualized in his statement quoted above.)

"I would urge most strongly that the notion of something 'outside' the universe should be dropped from all our ways of thinking, and that if we wish to use the label 'god' it should be used only in the above association of concepts: The universe constitutes everything there is. . . .

"But the main point I wish to bring out is that considerable progress can be made toward understanding man's relation to the universe. This can be done without any of the ancient beliefs and without 'faith.' The purely scientific approach to such issues as 'life,' 'death,' 'soul,' and so on, already reveals more in the way of remarkable conclusions than we might have expected. The picture is not complete, or anything like complete. Nor should we expect it to be, since it has become clear in recent years that science itself is still only at the beginning of the road. Recent studies of the ultrasmall in nuclear physics and of the ultralarge in astronomy have made it plain that there are whole worlds of understanding still to be opened up to us. And it is scarcely to be supposed that vitally new scientific knowledge will have no relation to the subject of our present discussion. There are some always ready to assert that science is a barren study, and that only with faith in the efficacy of ill-understood labels can the 'truth' be perceived. How it comes about that the universe revealed by painstaking scientific investigation is so incomparably grander than anything that the 'men of faith' have ever told us about, I have never yet heard tell.

"We started the present chapter by saying that life will be found empty unless the continuity of the human species is endowed with a sense of purpose. We saw that aims of economic sufficiency, of natural aspirations, may prove an adequate inducement for a time, but for a time only. In the long run a broader perspective is needed. Perhaps an answer can now be offered as to what this perspective might be. By continuing to search out the ways of the universe and of man's relation to the universe we shall be serving our deepest instincts and we shall be following a progressive line of development. In this can lie our aim.

"There are some indications that people are moving already in that direction. There is a looking outward from the earth, a desire of man to feel he has a part in the great play of the universe."[10]

However, in his lectures delivered at the University of Washington (State) in 1964 and published under the title "Of Men and Galaxies," Dr. Hoyle takes a less belligerent attitude in his stand that "any concept of a 'creator' standing outside the universe directing its processes should be disavowed," by making the following declaration:

"I am going to make a big hypothesis—that the emergence of intelligent life is *not a meaningless accident*. But I am not going to follow orthodox religions by presuming that I know what the meaning is. Intelligent life is such a remarkable phenomenon to emerge out of the basic physical laws that some connection seems implied, i.e. some correlation between laws and the consequences of the laws— what in common terms we would call *plan*." Whose *plan*? I ask.

---

10. *Man and Materialism*, by Fred Hoyle, Harper & Brothers Publishers, New York, 1956.

Albert Einstein

Albert Einstein had been accused by Cardinal O'Connell of Boston and by the *Osservatore Romano* of being an "atheist." Dr. Einstein spelled out his beliefs in very simple language as follows:

"In the first place, the human mind, no matter how highly trained, is not capable of grasping the Universe. We are like a little child entering a huge library. The walls are covered to the ceiling with books in many different tongues. The child knows that someone must have written these books. It does not know who or how. It does not understand the languages in which they were written. The child notes a definite plan in the arrangement of the books—a mysterious order which it does not comprehend, but only dimly suspects. That, it seems to me, is the attitude of the human mind towards God. And because I believe this, I am not an atheist."[11]

IV. RÉSUMÉ

A careful analysis of the statements made by Pope Pius XII, D'Arcy, Tillich, and Kaplan, representing the religionists, and Stetson, Jeans, Hoyle, Shapley, and Einstein, representing the scientists, show, on the whole, a surprising agreement on the question of *mutability and evolution* throughout the universe. There is, however a wide divergence in their points of view with respect to the acceptance on faith of the omniscience and omnipotence of God.

Dr. Paul Tillich argues that you cannot "prove" the existence of God by any known scientific formula, that the omniscience and omnipotence of God must be accepted on faith. Dr. Fred Hoyle, on the other hand, argues that God *is* the universe and that any concept of a "creator" standing apart and outside of the universe, directing its processes and density, should be disavowed. However, in his John Danz lectures, some eight years later he modified his uncompromising attitudes by admitting that "the emergence of Intelligent Life is not a meaningless accident" directed by blind physical laws.

Drs. Harlan T. Stetson and Sir James Jeans, for their part, are content to leave the matter of creation or creator to the philosophers or religionists since the subject lies in the realm of metaphysics rather than science. Dr. Harlow Shapley, in his turn, is noncommittal on this subject, but favors the proposition that in due time man may acquire the capacity to "assail such questions rationally." In effect, this is very much the position taken by D'Arcy. Dr. Albert Einstein is outspoken in his declaration that he is *not* an atheist.

The most interesting aspect in this controversy is the stand taken by the religionist Mordecai M. Kaplan. "Many people," he states, "cannot understand a concept of God in which He is regarded as working in and through nature."

11. *Einstein, Profile of the Man,* by Peter Michaelmore, Dodd Mead & Co., New York, 1962.

That, indeed, brings him closer to the views of Shapley and Hoyle than it does to Tillich or D'Arcy.

Taking it by and large, despite the differences of opinion on some basic subjects, the spirit of rapprochement between science and religion has grown to a marked degree during the four or five decades that have passed since the first joint declaration was made by a group of prominent scientists and religious leaders back in the month of June 1, 1923.

What Would a Scientific Religion Be Like?

H. G. MacPherson

THE WORLD IS a far different place than it was when the last of the great religions of the world was founded some 1,300 years ago. The literature that serves as the basis of the world's religions was composed long before the world was proved to be round. Religious traditions and liturgies involve a number of beliefs and assumptions incompatible with present-day scientific sophistication.

Certainly the founders and early embellishers of the religions are not to be blamed for this situation. On the other hand, modern man cannot be expected to shut his mind to all that has happened in the last thousand years. A simple solution to the dilemma would be to strike religion from our lives, and, indeed, some have done just that. However, many others feel a real need for the values and spiritual support that religion has traditionally provided.

Much attention has been given to altering the extent and content of religious doctrine to make it more relevant to modern life. My purpose runs in an opposite direction: to examine scientific attitudes and knowledge to see if they leave some room for religion, and, if they do, to try to discern what the basic elements of that religion might be.

I shall approach the question from the point of view of a physical scientist, not because the views of the scientist are particularly important in religion but because the scientist is probably the hardest to please in what he will allow as permissible religious content. Since not all scientists think alike, I shall look through the eyes of a particular scientist, which is to say my own.

I shall begin with the two aspects of science that provoke the most clashes with religous beliefs. One is the method of thought of the scientist. The other is the solid body of proven scientific knowledge.

Any person who has the instincts of a scientist is a doubter by nature. He distrusts all statements that appear arbitrary to him, and he is on constant lookout

216

for such statements. To accept a new fact, he must first be provided with carefully documented background information. He is especially reluctant to believe anything that appears to conflict with theories that have accurately described the relationship of previously verified events. He tends to believe what he has seen or what other trained observers have seen, provided all such events fit together in a natural way and can be correlated by general rules. Essentially all other reported events he classes as exceptions to the order observed in nature and therefore of doubtful verity.

This attitude seems, and is, very repressive. If it were the only significant characteristic of the scientist, he would be a very dull companion indeed, one who would dampen enthusiasm and discourage joy. Fortunately, most scientists possess other attributes that make them at least passable companions. Furthermore, great scientists have fertile imaginations and insatiable curiosities that drive them to new discoveries capable of surviving the scientist's own suspicious scrutiny.

It goes almost without saying that the scientists cannot accept most religious literature as fact. All the traditional religions are based on myths and legends that have a high content of miraculous or unnatural events. This situation is readily understandable because many of the stories were transmitted by word of mouth through generations of people steeped in superstition. The scientist cannot believe that these miracles or unnatural events really occurred; there is no verifiable supporting evidence, and they do not fit into the pattern of knowledge we now have of the physical world. If the scientist displays tolerance to such biblical stories as that of the virgin birth, a tenet common to several religions, it is on the same basis that he repeats the story of Santa Claus to his children.

A common ingredient of many religions is faith. If we mean by faith the acceptance of a set of ideas without proof, it must be admitted that faith has a place in everyone's life, for the world is too complicated to allow time for proof of every little step. However, faith, in the religious sense, is often interpreted to require blind acceptance of a complex set of beliefs—some of which involve the supernatural—and of a god possessing supernatural powers. The doubting nature of the scientist prevents him from having this kind of faith. When a complex of beliefs is held aloof from rational inquiry, the scientist is alienated.

I have already indicated that the scientist will accept new facts provided they reach his consciousness by a certain route, which may be designated by the term "controlled experiment." The experiment is like a play in which the stage setting is carefully and precisely arranged and the actors have well-known characteristics. When the curtain rises, the starting situation is specified exactly, even including the positions of the actors on the stage. Then the action is allowed to proceed without interference, and a trained observer watches what occurs. For the physical scientist, the actors are inanimate, or at least incapable of original thought and independent decision, and so the scientist expects the action to take place exactly

217

the same way each time the play is enacted. If the action is not the same in two successive playings, then the assumption is made that the initial conditions were not identical or that the actors have changed.

How, then, can the scientist believe that prayer can alter the course of events? If he is a good scientist, he must believe that the result of an experiment is determined completely by the physical conditions surrounding the experiment. If it were otherwise, the poor scientist would be in terrible shape. He would not know whether a negative result was obtained because of something he did or as a consequence of the prayer of the man in the next room. Imagine trying to derive a theory of gravity if a lead weight, instead of falling, should sometimes rise because of divine intercession!

It may be pointed out that many scientists do pray. I suspect that this is a manifestation of the fact that they are human beings as well as scientists. It is probable that most of the prayers said by scientists in public are of a ceremonial type, customary in the group, and done as a ritual that has social value among the human spirits assembled. Prayers are also said by scientists in deep privacy as an expression of their personal humility and their admitted inability to cope with all of the problems that face them. The true scientist, however, does not expect any physical intercession as a result of his prayer. The results he expects, or hopes for, are tone-setting or therapeutic in nature. If he prays at a public meeting, he can expect that the interruption provided by the prayer will momentarily bring the group to unified attention and to a common starting point for further proceedings. When he prays alone, he can expect psychological help from the relaxation afforded by the assumption of a submissive attitude. These are undoubtedly beneficial effects and may be of religious significance. Unfortunately, these events are likely to leave the scientist with some feelings of hypocrisy for engaging in the rites of a religion in which he lacks absolute faith.

A slightly different aspect of the conflict between science and religion arises from a comparison of the accumulated body of scientific knowledge with the beliefs, traditions, and practices of religion. The distinction between this view of the problem and that arising from consideration of the doubting nature of the scientist himself may seem a little contrived, but it becomes important when we consider the significance of the limits of science. There is a limitation not only on the areas of human experience that the scientist can investigate, but on the knowledge that can be accumulated about nature and the universe. In considering the restrictions imposed on religious belief by scientific knowledge, it is necessary to include the anticipated growth in scientific knowledge over the next few centuries. To anticipate such knowledge accurately is, of course, impossible, but we must do the best we can if we are to adopt religious ideas valid over a lifetime.

Take the belief that some people have in the physical existence of heaven or hell. Men have explored the entire surface of the earth and found neither place. Quite a bit is known about the interior of the earth, and much more will be learned in future years; no scientist expects to find a heavenly sanctuary there, or a habitable hell. Earthmen will probably complete exploration of the solar system within a hundred years, and scientists hold little hope of finding anywhere in the system conditions suitable for a heaven. Our present knowledge of the physical limits to speed of travel makes planets of stars other than the sun seem quite improbable as practical sites for an afterlife. In short, our present and anticipated knowledge of scientific facts would seem to eliminate the possibility of heaven as a real place where transformed humans can pursue activities that have any real appeal to us.

Another example of a conflict between religion and scientific knowledge lies in the story of the origin of the world. In the literature of many religions there are folktales about how it all started, but these tales are not compatible with present knowledge. An understanding of the physical world gained in the past half-century now allows plausible descriptions of the sequence of events. According to one popular theory, the universe started off at time zero as a relatively small ball of fire, with a concentration of radiant energy so great that it is difficult to imagine. Radiation pressure forced this ball of fire to expand at a very rapid rate. The ball cooled as it expanded, and the formation of the chemical elements and their condensation into the various forms of matter followed in a scientifically logical way. New knowledge about the universe is continually accumulating, and the scientific story of creation will continue to unfold for a long time to come.

What, then, are the limits of the scientist's domain? There seem to be two important ones. First is the probable limit of his ability to probe the universe and gain knowledge of its laws. For example, in regard to the scientific speculation about the early history of the universe, little attention has been given to the question of how the fireball came into being at time zero. The suggestion has been made that prior to the start of the expansion there was a contraction of the universe which led to the initial condition, ready for the current expansion. But even if one postulates an oscillating universe, alternately expanding and contracting, one's imagination must eventually stumble back to a time, however long ago, that the universe got started. It seems probable that science will never tell us for sure what was happening just before that beginning, or how the matter and energy and space that we call the universe came into being in the first place. Furthermore, although the scientist believes that the natural physical laws of the universe existed in their present form even at time zero, he cannot fully understand why these laws are as he has found them, rather than their being quite different. Hence, there are cosmic mysteries of the physical world that the scientist concedes to be beyond his powers of investigation and understanding, therefore outside his domain.

If one chooses, one can regard these regions beyond the domain of the scientist as the territory of a supreme deity. As Krishna says in the Bhagavad-Gita, "I am the source of the forthgoing of the whole universe and likewise the place of its dissolving. There is naught whatsoever higher than I. All this is threaded on me, as rows of pearls on a string."

Acceptance of such a thought can provide the comfort of a verbal description of a universe that has no gaps. One can complete the picture by saying, "God created the universe and its laws." If the scientist were to subscribe to this, he would do so with an awareness that he was substituting one mystery for another. He is rather likely to refer to this god in an allegorical sense, expressing his awe in contemplation of the grandeur of nature.

The second area that lies outside the domain of the scientist is that of animal consciousness. The essence of animal consciousness is the awareness of one's own existence, an awareness that is apparently common to all of the higher animals. The conscious animal learns that he exists by becoming aware of information received through the senses. He experiences an external world by feeling, hearing, tasting, smelling, and seeing it. His consciousness also allows him to be aware of judgments on whether the sensations are pleasant or hurtful. These judgments checked against past experience and basic biological urges such as hunger or sex, lead to feelings of fear, friendship, love, and hatred.

It takes only a small amount of reflection to realize that the phenomenon of conscious existence, which we believe to be beyond the scope of the scientist, is of more importance to us than any of the things that are within the scientist's domain. Science can deal only with the setting within which this conscious awareness exists. The setting largely determines the opportunity for a higher quality of existence. For example, the physical world in which the scientist operates determines the food we eat and how we get it, the clothing we wear, our housing, transportation, heat and refrigeration, sanitation, and medicine. Without our conscious awareness, however, all of these benefits of science and technology would be of no significance.

How sure are we that animal consciousness is not amenable to future scientific exploration, explanation, and synthesis? The physical scientist intuitively places this realm outside his area of investigative competence, but some biophysicists find the field challenging. For example, R. L. Sinsheimer has stated, "Indeed, it may be supposed that even the deepest mystery, the nature of mind and sensation and consciousness, will be understood in the end as a natural consequence of matter in a certain state of organization."

Even if this supposition should prove correct, there still would be the question of the nature and extent of the understanding of the physical basis of consciousness. In any case, it is probably safe to assume that in the foreseeable future man will not be able to synthesize an object or a being with a capability for consciousness approaching his own.

The quality of consciousness appears to vary a great deal among different people, and also changes during the life of each individual. Factors affecting the quality of consciousness include such things as inherent intellectual capability and the pattern of attitudes and habits that the person has assumed through past associations. What is referred to here as the human spirit encompasses the entire range of the quality and intensity of the individual. External manifestations of this spirit are the personality of the individual, his actions (as evidences of the mental choices he has made), and his communication with others, whether by verbal or other means.

Although a full understanding of the mechanism of consciousness lies outside the domain of the scientist, it is appropriate to examine the available evidence in order to try to discover some broad truths about consciousness and the human spirit. Since the richest source of evidence about the human spirit is subjective—obtained by examining our own thoughts and by making personal interpretations of other people's behavior—the scientist will squirm, for he has been trained to be objective. He will cringe at the lack of experimental controls. However, he would agree that it is better to look where the information is abundant rather than rule out all but the most sterile information as would be done if we limited ourselves to scientifically verifiable sources.

The spirit can be examined in several ways. One is by observation of people and other animals that possess the capability of consciousness; another is by listening to what people tell us about their thoughts, either verbally or in their writings; and a third is by introspection. For each of us, introspection should give the sharpest and least distorted picture, because it is a direct path involving a minimum of intervening interpretation. However, the variety of experience with conscious thought among different people is so great that we must consider the evidence from others as well.

The first observation to be noted is that the spirit either makes life joyous and satisfying or converts life into something considerably less than satisfactory. The happy feelings that we can appreciate are many. Some of them seem to come from purely physical sensations, but without conscious realization they would give hardly any satisfaction. A simple example is the joy of a flaming sunset, the variations of red and orange in the clouds. The transmission of these as radiant energy to the eye and conversion of the energy to an optical nerve impulse are all physical phenomena explained by science. The pleasure is something else again.

Another, somewhat more complex, example is the effect of an orchestral performance of a symphony. The members of the orchestra manipulate instruments that put sonic vibrations of different frequencies and various wave forms into the air. The vibrations are transmitted by compression waves to the ear of the listener, where they are translated into a mechanical motion of the eardrum, and the sensation is passed on to the brain by electrical impulses along nerves. These are all physical processes, scientifically understood and interesting to know about, but yielding no musical satisfaction. If the listener has never heard music of that kind before, his reaction is likely to be rather dull; a generous portion of musical education is required for the fullest enjoyment. It is clear that what makes the performance of the orchestra worthwhile is not the mechanical production of sonic vibrations, but the response to these vibrations in the consciousness of the listener.

Probably our greatest awareness of the wondrous importance of the spirit comes through the emotions. It is true that physiological changes accompany shifts in our emotions, but, for example, the effects of adrenalin in the blood do not seem important in comparison with the fear or anger that invades our conscious existence. Similarly, feelings of love and friendship are accompanied by physiological changes, but it is the conscious experience that is important to us.

A second important observation is that the spirit of an individual is not a fixed thing given him at birth and lasting unchanged until death. A person's spirit develops with age, and its direction and intensity of development depend strongly on the surrounding spirits with which it comes into contact. The attention now accorded to the application of "tender loving care" in early childhood attests to the common acceptance of the importance of early childhood experiences in the development of a well-adjusted person. On the other hand, if a person is brought up with people who are always bitter and cynical, it is unlikely that he will develop a warm and optimistic character. Similarly, the extent and type of education received by a person will strongly influence the quality of his consciousness and, thus, his spirit. For example, if a person does not learn to read easily, he can never absorb much of the wisdom and beauty that abounds in literature.

Although persistent and long lasting environmental influences are undoubtedly the most effective in molding character or developing one's spirit, strong effects of short-term encounters often occur. These apparently sudden shifts in patterns of thought may very well be preceded by longer-term influences that predispose a person to be susceptible, but there is no doubt that sudden changes of outlook do occur. The best known ones are in religious lore, such as the conversion of Paul or the dreams of Mohammed. However, most of us have had experiences, which others might consider trivial, that have had a strong influence on our pattern of thinking. Typically, our attention is focused on a particular remark or comment so that we establish it firmly in our minds, while the person who made the remark goes his way and rapidly forgets the occasion. The ever-present possibility of evoking, in our turn, significant changes in another person's spirit through a short-term contact is something to be remembered.

The development of a strong spirit seems to demand contact with other spirits. Enjoyment of life, which is one manifestation of a strong spirit, cannot be experienced to any great extent in isolation. A number of people like to think of themselves as going it alone but, if they reflect carefully, they will find that their goals and satisfactions are derived from previous contact with living spirits, if

222

not directly, then indirectly through reading or other remote means of influence. Similarly, their sense of achievement comes from the reaction of others.

As each of them thinks about his own spirit, the wonder of it grows. Here certainly is something more than just flesh and bone or nervous tissue. The question naturally occurs: "How can this complicated presence, above and beyond the physical world, disappear when we die?" Men have always been tormented by this conundrum, and it leads all of us to examine the possibility of immortality. Since animal consciousness is not at present explainable in terms of scientific concepts, are we not at liberty to assume that, whatever this spirit is, it can exist after death? This view would provide a great deal of comfort; perhaps it would be permissible to make whatever assumptions we like about something of such an uncertain nature. To please the scientist, however, the available evidence must be examined rigorously.

What evidence have we, the living, received from spirits of the departed? There is no scientifically verified evidence. The continued existence of spirits in a wholly spirit world, out of contact with living people, is an interesting concept, and may provide solace at the death of a loved one. It is, however, an assumption that the scientist cannot support.

There are other limits to the view of an afterlife of spirits. One of these is the thought that spirit is a quality developed during a person's life on earth, therefore probably specifically suited to earthly existence. Certainly the quality of consciousness develops from a small beginning during a person's lifetime; it cannot be considered as a something that has neither a beginning nor an end. It also seems to be true that the total quality that we call spirit can suffer some degradation in the old age of a person afflicted with a disease that causes deterioration of the brain. It is true that what we call character usually suffers less than the apparent intelligence of such a person, but the combination of character with intelligent response that usually is associated with the term "spirit" visibly diminishes in such cases before death occurs. For these reasons my own view is that a person's spirit is a quality associated with a person's life, a quality that develops for better or worse during that person's life. This spirit can live on only through the effects it works on other people's lives.

I have already noted the strong influence that spirits have on each other. The development of a strong spirit, or a benign spirit, depends on the leading and encouraging influence of other spirits. So a very real kind of immortality is available, in fact inescapable.

All religions contain within their structure a set of rules for behavior: definitions of the good and the bad. Many people, on losing faith in their religion, also lose faith in the arbitrary rules and seek new guides arrived at by logical method. As a scientist, I find an acceptable logic in the values that arise from interactions with fellow humans. Broadly speaking, I look at the effect of my actions and attitudes on the spirits of those about me. Where this influence helps those about me to meet the problems of life in healthy and constructive ways, then I regard my actions and attitudes as good. Conversely, if I do things that turn out to be harmful to the spirit of others, then I have done wrong.

The application of this principle is fairly straightforward. For example, the willful destruction of another spirit is obviously bad for that spirit and the rule "Thou shalt not kill" is quickly verified. Other instances of bad behavior are just as easily identified. From them it is possible to evolve a guide to what I *should* be doing, namely, those things that help to bring about the full development of other human spirits.

AUTHORS

Bemporad, Jack

Director of the Commission on Worship of the Union of American Hebrew Congregations, visiting lecturer at University of Pennsylvania in Department of Religion, visiting lecturer at College of New Rochelle in its Philosophy Department, visiting lecturer at the Hebrew Union College—Jewish Institute of Religion, in Department of Philosophy.

Campbell, John W.

Editor of *Analog*.

Cole, LaMont C.

Professor of ecology at Cornell University.

Einstein, Albert (1879–1955)

He received the Nobel Prize for scientific work in 1921, when he was still a member of the Prussian Academy of Sciences in Berlin. He came to America in 1933 and accepted a position at the Institute for Advanced Study in Princeton, New Jersey. Many believe that he ranks with Galileo and Newton in the history of scientific thought.

Eiseley, Loren

Chairman, Department of Anthropology, University of Pennsylvania.

Etkin, William

Associate professor of biology of the City College of New York and research associate professor in the Department of Anatomy, Einstein Medical College.

Ferry, W. H.

Vice president of the Fund for the Republic and the Center for the Study of Democratic Institutions.

Gittelsohn, Roland B.

Senior rabbi of Temple Israel, Boston, and author of several books, including *Wings of the Morning*, and *The Meaning of Judaism*.

Haybittle, John

Physicist, Addenbrookes Hospital, Cambridge, England.

Heitler, W.

Professor of physics, University of Zurich. With the late Fritz London, he showed that quantum mechanics provides a natural explanation of the binding of neutral atoms in such molecules as H_2.

Hertz, Karl H.

Professor of sociology, Wittenberg University, Springfield, Ohio.

MacPherson, H. G.

Deputy director of Oak Ridge National Laboratory at Oak Ridge, Tennessee.

Posner, Harry

Free lance writer on scientific issues.

Russell, Bertrand (1872–1970)

Born in England, he was educated at Trinity College, Cambridge. In 1931 he succeeded to the earldom, becoming the third Lord Russell. In 1951 he was awarded the Nobel Prize for Literature. His career has established him as one of the most brilliant and original contemporary philosophers and mathematicians.

Townes, Charles H.

Provost and professor of physics at MIT. He won a Nobel Prize in 1964.

Weinberg, Alvin M.

Director of Oak Ridge National Laboratory. His article "Can Technology Replace Social Engineering" was originally presented as the acceptance speech for the 1966 University of Chicago Alumni Award.

SOME DIFFICULT TERMS

"ad infinitum"—without end or limit.

anthropomorphic—described or thought of as having a human form or human characteristics.

antinomy—a contradiction between two apparently equally valid principles or between inferences correctly drawn from such principles.

226

cosmology—a branch of philosophy that deals with the universe as an orderly system; also a branch of astronomy that deals with the origin, structure, and space-time relationships of the universe.

ethnocentric—regarding one's own race or cultural group as superior to others.

eugenics—a science that deals with the improvement (as by control of human mating) of hereditary qualities of a race or breed.

"exclusion principle"—a principle in physics—no two electrons in an atom or molecule will be exactly equivalent.

Luddite—one of a group of early nineteenth-century English workmen destroying laborsaving machinery as a protest.

Moloch—a semitic deity worshiped through the sacrifice of children.

omnipotent—all-powerful.

phenomenological—pertaining to the philosophical study of the progressive development of mind.

Promethean—relating to Prometheus, a Titan in Greek legend who steals fire from heaven as a gift for man.

Stoic—not affected by passion or feeling; relating to the Stoics, members of a school of philosophy founded by Zeno about 300 B.C.E., holding that the wise man should be free from passion, unmoved by joy or grief, and submissive to natural law.

READING LIST

Barbour, Ian, *Issues in Science and Religion* (PRENTICE-HALL, 1966).

Barbour, Ian (ed.), *Science and Religion* (HARPER, 1968).

Burke, John (ed.), *The New Technology and Human Values* (WADSWORTH, 1967).

Clarke, Arthur, *The Nine Billion Names of God* (HARCOURT, BRACE & WORLD, undated).

Corliss, William, *Mysteries of the Universe* (CROWELL, 1967).

Diebold, John, *Man and the Computer* (PRAEGER PUBLISHERS, 1969).

Eiseley, Loren, *The Immense Journey* (VINTAGE, 1957).

Ellul, Jacques, *The Technological Society* (ALFRED KNOPF, 1964).

Ferkiss, Victor C., *Technological Man* (GEORGE BRAZILLER, 1969).

Ginzberg, Eli (ed.), *Technology and Social Change* (COLUMBIA, 1964).

Gittelsohn, Roland, *Man's Best Hope* (RANDOM HOUSE, 1961).

Haselden, Kyle, *Morality and the Mass Media* (BROADMAN, 1968).

Hillegas, Mark, *The Future as Nightmare: H. G. Wells and the Anti-Utopians* (OXFORD, 1967).

Morison, Elting, *Men, Machines, and Modern Times* (MIT PRESS, 1966).

Mumford, Lewis, *The Myth of the Machine: Technics and Human Development* (HARCOURT, BRACE, & WORLD, 1967).

Mumford, Lewis, *Technics and Civilization* (HARCOURT, BRACE & WORLD, 1963).

Plaut, Gunther, *Judaism and the Scientific Spirit* (UAHC, 1962).

Rosenfeld, Albert, *The Second Genesis: The Coming Control of Life* (PRENTICE-HALL, 1969).

Russell, Bertrand, *Mysticism and Logic* (ANCHOR, 1957).

Warner, Aaron, Dean Morse, and Alfred Eichner (eds.), *The Impact of Science and Technology* (COLUMBIA, 1965).

White, Hugh, Jr. (ed.), *Christians in a Technological Era* (SEABURY, 1964).